GREGORIUS

The Good Sinner

GREGORIUS
The Good Sinner

HARTMANN von AUE

Bilingual Edition

Translated by
SHEEMA ZEBEN BUEHNE

Introduction by
HELEN ADOLF

FREDERICK UNGAR PUBLISHING CO.
NEW YORK

Introduction

The medieval tale presented here, written by Hartmann von Aue, is known to students of literature as *Gregorius*. The epithet *the good sinner* or *on the rock* has on occasion been added. Thomas Mann used an epithet which became the title of his book, *Der Erwählte 'The Chosen One'* (titled in English *The Holy Sinner*), an epithet that is particularly appropriate. What accounts for the interest of the public in the subject matter of this tale of Gregorius—from the days of Hartmann von Aue in the thirteenth century to modern times?

It is a story of extremes, arousing ambivalent feelings: Gregorius, born of sibling incest, is exposed to death but rescued; he is raised to be a monk, yet he attains knighthood, only to commit incest unwittingly with his mother; a penitent for seventeen years on a rock in the sea, he is called miraculously to preside over the See of St. Peter. Why was he chosen by both poet and public to become the hero of a story? Hartmann, who had upheld the facile courtly solution to the problems of life in his earlier Arthurian romances, strikes a note of protest in *Gregorius*. For the stark extremes of sinful lust, horrible austerity, and wondrous exaltation are not present for their own sake, as is the case in a melodrama. Originating in the distant past, they incorporate in the universal language of symbols certain theological and psychological truths; that is, they treat of the secrets between God and man, or of man's spiritual endowment and the fleshly foundations of that endowment.

Some seven hundred years elapsed between the first appearance of the Gregorius motif in a Coptic tale and Hartmann's version, somewhat more than seven hundred years between Hartmann and Thomas Mann. The role of the incest motif has changed, and the legend has undergone a triple transformation.

Incest, now the bane of slum life but once the quasi-hieratic privilege of dynasties, is, according to depth psychology, either a regression to phases of infantile sexuality or a symbol for the successful union of opposites. In legend, however, incest appears, on first sight, to mean simply "the forbidden"; it is the breach of a taboo so formidable that the transgressor becomes an outcast. Upon closer scrutiny, we may recognize incest as a cipher for lust (*in-cestus* is nothing other than *non-castus*), and this interpretation makes us understand the attraction that the Oedipus legend, the Gregorius legend, or any other incest legend, must have exerted on the minds of Christian theologians. In the days when dogmas were being shaped, incest may have become *a cipher for original sin,* the sin of our origin. To be sure, it was self-will, self-love, *superbia* that had caused Adam's Fall; but self-love led to lust, and, according to St. Augustine, each act of lustful procreation bequeathed Adam's sin to each subsequent generation. This cipher, applied to the early Coptic tale, the proto-Gregorius, would indicate that man, engendered in sin (incest), is bound to repeat that sin himself; however, he is able to remove the "rust of sin" by means of sharpest ascetic practice. Indeed, this was the view of the Oriental Fathers. Their ascetic saints (Alexius under the Stairs, Simon on the Pillar, John i.e., Gregorius on

the Rock) did not do "penance" for individual sin but restored to human nature the splendor of Paradise that
had been forfeited by Adam's Fall. Self-imposed morti-
fication was for them the road to Life Eternal, to a
superhuman status which caused earth and heaven to
rejoice.

Under the changed conditions of twelfth-century
Christendom in the West, the grandiose though harsh
Eastern outlook was modulated through the efforts of
the great Gregories on the papal throne: The Church
became a tower of strength, an institution that offered
sinful man certainty of grace through penance. The
ascetic on the rock became Gregory, the good sinner.
Hartmann, perhaps more than any other German poet
of the Middle Ages, was aware of the dilemma that
faced man and of the sacramental institutions that
alone offered salvation. Like a bridge flung over an abyss,
the prologue to his *Gregorius* connects the present and
the past: "Never despair of God's mercy, O sinners!
This would constitute the sin of Judas, a sin against the
Holy Ghost. See how Gregorius trod the narrow and
awful path of penance and obtained more than pardon
. . ." Pardon for what? In Hartmann's times a child
was not responsible for incest committed by his parents,
nor was he responsible for incest he himself committed
unwittingly. Therefore, there will always remain the
painful disproportion between Gregorius' transgression
—for his real sin is disclosed as that of *superbia*—and
his punishment, and, correspondingly, the disproportion
between the language of the symbols involved and the
psychological interpretation superimposed upon them by
Hartmann.

Compared to Hartmann's *Gregorius* with its serious
solicitude, Thomas Mann's version—anachronistic,

parodistic, ironic—may sound even blasphemous, but it
is based on a solid rationale. To Mann, the case of
Gregorius, the sinner, becomes the case history of a
neurosis, according to the theories of the later Freud;
for what else is "incest" if not a fixation on, or a regression to, phases of infantile sexuality? Grigorss, the
protagonist of Mann's story, having gratified his incestuous wishes (only half-unconsciously), and having
thereby brought on the recurrence of compulsive seizures
of guilt and despair, "collects" himself once he has become fully conscious of the situation, and embarks on
a ruthless but highly successful self-analysis. Instead of
the couch, there is the rock; fettered to it, the Id must
shrink (and shrink it does—to the size of a hedgehog),
to let the Ego grow. After seventeen years (an analysis
takes time!) the super-Freud is made pope, and knowing
as he does how our spirit is rooted in the flesh, he becomes a very great pope indeed, able to dissolve and,
hence, absolve all the neuroses of Christendom. Our
times prefer the strident, even the absurd, to the use
of muted strings, to the conciliatory attitude that cre-
ates beauty!

Professor Buehne's translation follows Hartmann von
Aue with utmost accuracy. Since the modern translator,
in contradistinction to the medieval one, is pledged to
the strictest textual fidelity—no omissions, no additions,
no changes—her task was far from simple. One might
even say that it was twofold: she had to translate from
German into English, and from a medieval idiom into
a modern one. Gifted with a musician's fine ear for
rhythm and rhyme and with a poetic feeling for words,
she is equally sensitive to the nuances, overtones, and
ambiguities of meaning. It seems to me that the prob-
lem of making Hartmann, the medieval Swabian knight,

talk English has been solved by Professor Buehne with artistry and beauty. Deftly she shifts with him from deep concern to elegant banter, from naïveté to sophistication, while using a language that by its subtleness and scope throws a thin veil of irony over the primitive contours.

Read the story of Gregorius; remain aware of the original meaning of the legend, of its medieval aspect, and of its modern implications; but above all, let the whole act on your mind and imagination. Look at it as if it were an ancient tapestry or an illuminated manuscript. Towering over the scanty written lines of the parchment are great and sombre allegorical figures among whom moves a little human figure: the foundling, the schoolboy, the monk, the knight, the duke, the penitent, the pope. Meanwhile, in the corners of the page, simple folk enjoy the amenities of life according to the season. Are we really separated from the inception of the theme by more than a millennium?

HELEN ADOLF

Professor Emerita
The Pennsylvania State University

CONTENTS

Preface

Over a decade ago, when I first read Thomas Mann's quasi-parody, *Der Erwählte,* I became fascinated by the idea of translating Hartmann's *Gregorius,* "the holy sinner," into English that would somehow recreate the atmosphere of the original: its naïve sophistication, its complex simplicity, its profundity and humor. In *Gregorius* the mystery of religious faith transcends simple hagiologic legend in the rich interplay of subject matter: the realm of the moralistic-didactic with its theological niceties; *aventiûre,* the chivalric world of Arthurian tradition, in which the soldier, *miles gloriosus,* has become the knight, *miles religiosus;* the realm of the lowly commoner, crude servant to church and court; and then, *minne,* 'courtly love' or, in its highest reaches, mystery as well as mysticism, love of God. I was challenged by Hartmann's language, that composite of rhythmic mellifluence, stylized formulae, dramatic dialogue, and surges of pure lyricism. Yet beyond the charm of language and music, image, pun, and ambiguity, there was the appeal of the primary human relationships presented with the starkness of the tragic quality of Greek or Hebrew literature but wearing the garb of the Middle Ages. Above all, I was drawn by the counterpoint on the eternal theme of *de profundis clamavi* which underlies the religious mystery. Only he who despairs of God is beyond redemption. The man who does not despair of God is saved, no matter what other crimes he may have committed—even incest, that medieval epitome of hideous sin. Man's desperate need to be reconciled with God drives him to take upon himself temporal suffering in order to ward off endless suffering in a world to come. In our age, when the approach to the concept of an afterlife differs from that of the Middle Ages, the archetypical images of the Gregorius legend are still meaningful, although the emphasis has shifted. Today, through depth analysis, we know more about the world of man's unconscious, the theater of man's so-called sinful nature; but perhaps we know less about man's reconciliation with God.

Every work of a distant age breathes a breath of strangeness, since it tells of a way of life that no longer exists; every translation will inevitably convey that strangeness, but the constants of human emotion, thought, and experience will ring true. Despite the strangeness of the medieval trappings, intrinsic to *Gregorius* is a deeply rooted faith in God Who works miracles, and there is truth in the therapeutic approach: Sinful man, if he but have faith, may obtain grace of God and his own salvation through true repentance and atonement. Since the miracles of God in our miraculous age of outer-space navigation, earth satellites, and moon landings, strike a strange note in a world ruled by mechanics, and lend themselves readily to ridicule, it seemed of paramount importance to try to recapture the natural childlike reverence and simple sincerity of the Middle High German text.

My translation was undertaken after intensive study of the variant readings, particularly with respect to the much-disputed Prologue. To the best of my knowledge, it is the first metrical translation in English of

Hartmann's *Gregorius* in its entirety. There has been so much scholarly work done on *Gregorius* that there is no need here to air linguistic, philological, literary-historical, mythological, psychological, or other problems.* Suffice it to say, "The poem's the thing."

A poem stands on its own merits, but the passage of eight centuries may cloud the reader's eyes, dim his hearing, and slow down his perceptions. Spectacles and a hearing aid may help to overcome the inroads of time, but if one is burdened by too many extraneous aids, the enjoyment of poetry, as of life itself, ceases; first weariness and then rejection may set in. For that reason I have reduced the number of interpretive notes to a minimum. Sir John Denham once said, "Poesie is of so subtile a spirit, that in pouring out of one Language into another, it will all evaporate; and if a new spirit be not

---

* In 1951 I wrote to Professor Edwin Zeydel, informing him of my intention to translate Hartmann's *Gregorius*. At that time Professor Zeydel had not yet begun his own translation which he later published with the collaboration of Professor Bayard Quincy Morgan: *Gregorius, A Medieval Oedipus Legend*, by Hartmann von Aue, translated into rhyming couplets with Introduction and Notes, University of North Carolina Studies in the Germanic Languages and Literatures, No. XIV (Chapel Hill: The University of North Carolina Press, 1955). I was long tempted to lay aside my own work, listed in the *PMLA* issues of Research in Progress of April, 1952, and April, 1953; but through the encouragement of Professors Helen Adolf and Philip A. Shelley, I continued (although at a slower pace than that of Professor Zeydel). The virtue of the Zeydel-Morgan edition rests in the fact that it gives a clear survey of the literary-historical background of the thematic material. However, the translation itself, in my judgment, fails to reproduce Hartmann's poetic character. Moreover, it is incomplete, lacking approximately one-twentieth of the text. My dissertation (The Pennsylvania State University, 1960), "A Metrical Translation of *Gregorius, The Good Sinner*, by Hartmann von Aue, with Critical and Interpretive Notes," points out infelicities and misinterpretations in the Zeydel-Morgan translation.

added in the transfusion, there will remain nothing but a *caput mortuum*." The work of the translator lies not in counting words or syllables, but in so pouring the δυναμις from one vessel into the other that the original is metamorphosed into the new language, at ease, as it were, in the new idiom. If the modern translator with his quickened awareness of the levels of inner being is able to re-create the interplay of the different realms of the subject matter, and if at the same time he can give poignancy to those moments of universal experience in the epic when man faces the ever-frightening archetypes, then he will have achieved his aim.

S. Z. B.

Rutgers University
Camden, N. J.

Hartmann von Aue and
Gregorius

Of Hartmann von Aue, the man, little is known. There is disagreement about almost every so-called "fact" in his life. He may have been a Swabian, but he was probably Swiss (Alemannic). His birth and death dates are unknown, but it is assumed that he was born some time between 1160 and 1170, and that he died not before 1210 and not after 1220. Historically, he appears on the scene in the 1180's and disappears about 1210. It is assumed that at least part of his education was received at a monastery school, perhaps at Reichenau. It seems highly probable that he served, as a young knight, under a feudal lord to whom he was greatly attached. He may have taken part in a crusade; if so, there is dispute about which one, whether that of 1189 or, what is more likely, that of 1197. There is decided disagreement about the dating of his works, less disagreement about their chronological sequence. It is unknown whether or not he ever married. In his lyrics, the love he expresses for his lady remains unrequited; but, he says, this is so only because of his own unworthiness and shortcomings. Much more significant for Hartmann is the feeling he expresses for his feudal liege. Upon the death of his master, he seems to have undergone an inner crisis which may have led him to a crusade.

It is generally agreed that *Erec, Das Büchlein*, the love lyrics, and the poems dealing with the crusades belong to his first period; *Gregorius* and *Der arme Heinrich*, to the second period; *Iwein* belongs to the third period, although parts of it may have been written earlier. It is more or less accepted that *Gregorius* was written between 1187 and 1195, but modern scholarship tends to accept the latter date.

There is little doubt among scholars about the source of Hartmann's epic *Gregorius*. In the twelfth century versions of an old French poem appeared, purporting to be the life of a holy pope, *un bon pecheor*. Six manuscripts exist of two basic French versions. Friedrich Neumann's opinion is that even a few of the existing parallelisms suffice to convince the reader that *Gregorius* stems from a *Grégoire*. It would be no disgrace for Hartmann if it were indeed so. In *Erec* and *Iwein* he followed Chrétien de Troyes, but he created his own tone. Likewise, in *Gregorius* he added his own turn of phrase, his own psychological touches, his own deeply religious sentiments.

The first critical edition of the text of *Gregorius*, made by Karl Lachmann in 1838 before the discovery of some of the better manuscripts, does not contain the Prologue. It was not until 1873 that Hermann Paul, the foremost editor of *Gregorius*, issued his invaluable edition of the entire work. Subsequent editions followed until his death, whereupon Albert Leitzmann took over. Ludwig Wolff, whose edition appeared in 1959, continues the Paul-Leitzmann tradition. In a masterly fashion, Friedrich Neumann in 1958 re-edited Feodor Bech's annotated edition of 1891. I have made use of as many editions, editors, commentators, etc., as possible, but the body of my translation is based on Paul's fourth edition of 1910.

The best modern German translations are those of Reinhard Fink, in 1939, and Burkhard Kippenberg, in 1959, the former in sturdy prose, the latter in unrhymed tetrameter-trimeter lines.

GREGORIUS

(Prolog)

Mîn herze hât betwungen
dicke mîne zungen
daz si des vil gesprochen hât
daz nâch der werlde lône stât:
daz rieten im diu tumben jâr.
nû weiz ich daz wol vür wâr:
swer durch des helleschergen rât
den trôst ze sîner jugent hât
daz er dar ûf sündet,
als in diu jugent schündet,   10
und er gedenket dar an:
'dû bist noch ein junger man,
aller dîner missetât
der wirt noch vil guot rât:

GREGORIUS, THE GOOD SINNER

Prologue[1]

The poet warns the reader against putting off
penance. He encourages him by an allegory to
seek God's grace and to shun the deadly sin of
Despair.

My heart has often led my tongue
Astray in what it's said or sung,
Persuading it to give acclaim
To worldly prize and worldly aim.
So counseled me my foolish youth.*[2]
Now full well I know this truth:
Who takes the Devil as advocate
And sins, consoled in youth's estate
By thinking he'll yet be forgiven
For crimes to which he now is driven—   **10**
Thus reflecting to his fill:
"You are but a young man still;
Be not concerned about your sinning;
There's ample time for fresh beginning;

---

[1] See appendix.
[2] An asterisk refers the reader to the Notes. Each reference is listed under the number of the line in which the
asterisk occurs. Wherever the line number of the English
translation differs from the equivalent line of the original,
the number of the latter follows in parentheses.

du gebüezest sị in dem alter wol',
der gedenket anders dannẹ er sol.
er wirt es lîhtẹ entsetzet,
wandẹ in des willen letzet
diu êhafte nôt,
sô der bitterlîche tôt   20
den vürgedanc richet
und im daz alter brichet
mit einem snellen ende.
der gnâden ellende
hât danne den bœsern teil erkorn.
und wære aber er geborn
von Adâme mit Abêle
und solde im sîn sêle
weren âne sünden slac
unz an den jungisten tac,   30
sô hætẹ er niht ze vil gegeben
umbe daz êwige leben
daz anegenges niht enhât
und ouch niemer zegât.
   Durch daz wærẹ ich gerne bereit
ze sprechenne die wârheit
daz gotes wille wære
und daz diu grôze swære
der süntlîchen bürde
ein teil ringer würde   40
die ich durch mînẹ unmüezikeit
ûf mich mit worten hân geleit.
wan dâ enzwîvel ich niht an:
als uns got an einem man
erzeiget und bewæret hât,
so enwart nie mannes missetât
ze dirre werlde sô grôz,
er enwerdẹ ir ledic unde blôz,
ob sị in von herzen riuwet
und sich niht wider niuwet.   50
   Von dem ich iu nû sagen wil,
des schulde was grôz unde vil

You'll make amends when you are old"—
His thoughts are not of proper mold.
Such comfort he may lightly lose,
For he will not be free to choose
Through force of dire necessity,*
When bitter death immutably   20
Inflicts on him swift punishment
And, destroying his intent,*
Brings his life to a sudden close.
The wretch, bereft of God's grace, chose
On greater evil to lay hold.
If he were Adam's son of old,
A second* Abel, and his soul
Since then he had kept clean and whole,
Lasting sinless without sway
To the very Judgment Day,   30
He'd not have made a sacrifice
Too great for life in Paradise
That never had beginning, nor
Will cease from being ever more.
(Hence gladly shall I* not refrain ³⁵
From voicing truth,* this end to gain:
That God's own will may come to pass,
And that the burdensome great mass
Of sins that on my back I've placed ³⁹
Through the idle words I've traced   40
And rhymed in idle poetry
May rest less heavily on me.
Of this I have no doubt whatever:
Man's evil deeds in this world never*
Waxed so great that he could not
Slough off his sins and of their blot
Be free by feeling true remorse*   √
And not renewing his sinful course—
As God has surely manifested
In one man's case clearly attested.   50
    The man whose tale I now begin
Was guilty of such heinous sin,

daz si vil starc ze hœrennę ist,
wan daz man si durch einen list
niht verswîgen getar:
daz dâ bî neme war
älliu sündigiu diet
die der tiuvel verriet
ûf den wec der helle,
ob ir deheiner welle   60
diu gotes kint mêren
und selbe wider kêren
ûf der sælden strâze,
daz er den zwîvel lâze
der manigen versenket.
swer sich bedenket
houbethafter missetât
der er vil lîhte manige hât,
sô tuot er wider dem gebote,
und verzwîvelt er an gote   70
daz er sîn niht enruoche,
ob er genâde suoche,
und entriuwet niemer wider komen:
sô hât der zwîvel im benomen
den wuocher der riuwe.
daz ist diu wâre triuwe
die er ze gote solde hân:
buoze nâch bîhte bestân.
wan diu vil bitter süeze
twinget sîne vüeze   80
ûf den gemeinlîchen wec:
der enhât stein noch stec,
mos gebirge noch walt,
der enhât ze heiz noch ze kalt.
man vert in ânes lîbes nôt
und leitet ûf den êwigen tôt.
    Sô ist der sælden strâze
in eteslîcher mâze
beide rûch und enge.
die muoz man die lenge   90

The listener might well demur
To hear it told; but I'd incur
A wrong if I suppressed this tale,
For it could be of some avail
To sinful men for this good reason:
Of all who through the Devil's treason
Are on their way straight down to Hell,
A single sinner might hear tell   60
Of this tale, wish to repent,
God's children's ranks this way augment,
And, choosing Heaven's road, forswear
His sinful doubting and despair*—
The downfall* of much of mankind.
  Who calls the deadly sins* to mind,
Aware perhaps that oftentimes
He has committed many crimes,
Breaks the Commandment once again
If he despairs of God and then   70
Believes that God has no concern
For him and he can not return
To grace* though he should strive for it.
Despair* robs him of benefit
That through repentance would be his.
Man's moral obligation is—
The duty he owes God alone—
First to confess and then atone.
The sweetness that bears bitter fruit*
Tempts him to tread the easier route   80
And lightfootedly to err:
No narrow paths, no rocks occur;
No forest, fens, or heights appear;
No heat, no cold does one feel here.
Effortless, with easy breath,
One travels it to eternal death.
  But how different from this*
Is the road to heavenly bliss!
This road is narrow and is rough.
One wanders wearily enough,   90

wallen unde klimmen,
waten unde swimmen,
unz daz si hin leitet
dâ si sich wol breitet
ûz disem ellende
an ein vil süezez ende.
den selben wec geriet ein man:
zer rehten zît er entran
ûz der mordære gewalt.
er was komen in ir behalt: 100
dâ hâten si in nider geslagen
und im vrevellîche entragen
aller sîner sinne kleit
und hâten in an geleit
vil marterlîche wunden.
ez was zuo den stunden
sîner sêle armuot vil grôz.
sus liezen si in vingerblôz
unde halp tôt ligen.
do enhâte im got niht verzigen   110
sîner gewonlîchen erbarmekeit
und sande im disiu zwei kleit,
gedingen unde vorhte,
diu got selbe worhte
daz si im ein schirm wæren
und allen sündæren:
vorhte daz er erstürbe,
gedinge daz er iht verdürbe.
vorhte liez in dâ niht ligen.
doch wære er wider gesigen,   120
wan daz in der gedinge
machete alsô ringe
daz er doch weibende saz:
dar zuo sô starcte in baz
diu geistlîche triuwe
gemischet mit der riuwe.
si tâten im vil guotes
und ervurpten in des bluotes.

Climbing its entire length.
One wades, one swims with all one's strength
Until it brings the pilgrim where
It widens beautiful and fair
Out of this exile and life's throes,
Revealing then a most sweet close.
   Now on this road there chanced a man.*
From murderers' attack he ran,
Escaping in a timely hour.
He had been held in their dread power: **100**
They'd struck him down with violence
And robbed him in their impudence
Of all the raiment that he wore,
And tortured him both sick and sore,
With many an agonizing wound.
His anguished soul upon that swooned—
Its destitution was so great.
Fully naked was his state
When they left him there half dead.
   Then God forsook him not and shed   **110**
His wonted mercy on him there,
And for raiment sent this pair:
Hope and Fear,* these two God sent
Whom He fashioned with intent
To clothe and shield not him alone,
But all sinners who will atone:
Fear of death and his damnation;
Hope of life and his salvation.
Fear roused him up from where he lay;
Yet he'd have fallen down straightway   **120**
Were it not that Hope upstarted
And caused him to be so lighthearted
That quivering with life at length
He sat upright. He gained more strength
From Spiritual Faith combined
With Repentance of true kind.
Great good they did unto him then
And cleansed him free of blood again.

si guzzen im in die wunden sîn
beidiu öl unde wîn: 130
diu salbę ist lindę und tuot doch wê,
daz öl diu gnâde, der wîn diu ê,
die der sündære haben muoz:
sô wirt im siechtuomes buoz.
alsus huop in bî sîner hant
diu gotes gnâdę als si in vant
ûf ir miltez ahselbein
und truoc in durch ruoche hein.
dâ wurden im verbunden
sîne verchwunden   140
daz er âne mâsen genas
und sît ein wârer kemphe was,
er einę über al die kristenheit.
noch enhân ich iu niht geseit,
welh die wunden sint gewesen
der er sô kûme ist genesen,
wie er die wunden emphie
und wie er sich ir ergie
âne den êwigen tôt.
des ist ze hœrenne nôt   150
und ze merkennę in allen
die dâ sint vervallen
under bercswæren schulden,
ob er ze gotes hulden
dannoch wider gâhet,
daz in got gernę emphâhet.
wan sîner gnâden ist sô vil
daz er des niene wil
und ez gar verboten hât
daz man durch deheine missetât   160
an im iht zwîvelhaft bestê.
ez enist dehein sünde mê,
man enwerdę ir mit der riuwe
ledic unde niuwe,
schœne unde reine,
niuwan der zwîvel eine:

Into his bitter wounds, so sore,
Oil and wine both did they pour;   130
The balm is painful yet benign.*
The oil is Grace; God's Law, the wine
To which the sinful man must yield;
Thus will he be of sickness healed.

   God's Grace drew him by the hand
Upon her gentle shoulder, and,
As she found him, with all care
She bore him home to nurse him there.
In such way were his fell wounds bound
That he recovered whole and sound,   140
Unscarred, and has become since then
A true Defender, lord of men,
Above all Christians elevated.

   I've not yet told you, nor related
The nature of these wounds that now
He'd scarce recovered from, nor how
He came to them and stayed alive,
Nor how he managed to survive
Without eternal death. There's need
For everyone to hear and heed—   150
For all who fall and wilt and cower
Beneath their sinful deeds that tower
Mountain-high—if such a one
Will none the less make haste and run
To seek God's grace, he'll be restored
And gladly welcomed by the Lord.
God's grace is of such bounteous store,
It never is His will—nay more,
He quite forbade it for all time—
That man, no matter what his crime,   160
Despair of Him in any way.

   From every other sin one may,
Through true repentance, grow to be
Cleansed and healed and pure and free;
But of Despair this is not true.
For it alone there is no rue.*

der ist ein mortgalle
zem êwigen valle
den nieman mac gesüezen
noch wider got gebüezen.   170
   Der dise rede berihte,
in tiusche getihte,
daz was von Ouwe Hartman.
hie hebent sich von êrste an
diu seltsænen mære
von dem guoten sündære.

Despair is bitter, deadly gall
That leads to man's eternal fall.
One can not sweeten it a whit,
Nor make amends to God for it.   170
   Hartmann von Aue, it was he
Who rhymed these lines of poetry;
In German verse this tale he told.
And now this strange tale will unfold
How our good sinner went astray
And was redeemed in wondrous way.

Ez ist ein wälhischez lant,
Equitânjâ genant,
und lît dem merę unverre:
des selben landes herre   180
gewan bî sînem wîbe
zwei kint diu an ir lîbe
niht schœner mohten sîn,
einen sun und ein tohterlîn.
der kinde muoter starp,
dô si in daz leben vol erwarp.
dô diu kint wâren
komen ze zehen jâren,
do ergreif den vater ouch der tôt.
dô er im sîn kunft enbôt   190
sô daz er in geleite,
dâ er von siecheite
sich des tôdes entstuont,
dô tet er sam die wîsen tuont:
zehant er besande
die besten von dem lande
den er getrûwen solde
und in bevelhen wolde
sîne sêlę und ouch diu kint.

CHAPTER I

Gregorius' Parentage and Birth

The widowed ruler of a realm in Aquitaine dies, leaving two young children, a son and a daughter.

There is within the French domain
A land that's known as Aquitaine;
It lies not distant from the sea.
The lord who held this realm in fee   180
Two children by his consort had,
A little daughter and a lad
Who were so ravishingly fair,
Their beauty was beyond compare.
Scarce had their mother given them birth
When death recalled her from this earth.
The children saw time go its way
Till ten years passed—then came the day ✓
That Death made known his presence dire
And laid his hold upon their sire.   190
The father, seeing Death encroaching,
Conscious of his end approaching—
For mortal ill had seized him too—
Did then as all wise men will do.
Straightway he summoned to his side
Those men in whom he could confide,
The noblest leaders of the land,
To trust them with his last command:
To tend his soul and children too.

nû daz si vür in komen sint,　　　　　　　200
mâge man und dienestman,
sîniu kint sach er dô an:
diu wâren gelîche
sô rehte wünneclîche
gerâten an dem lîbe
daz einem herten wîbe
ze lachenne wære geschehen,
ob si si müese an sehen.
　　Daz machete sînem herzen
vil bitterlîchen smerzen:　　　　　　　210
des herren jâmer wart sô grôz
daz im der ougen regen vlôz
nider ûf die bettewât.
er sprach: 'nû enist des niht rât,
ich enmüeze von iu scheiden.
nû solde ich mit iu beiden
alrêrst vreuden walten
und wünneclichen alten.
der trôst ist nû zegangen:
mich hât der tôt gevangen.'　　　　　　220
nu bevalh er si bî handen
den herren von den landen
die durch in dar wâren komen.
hie wart grôz weinen vernomen.
ir jâmer zuo den triuwen
schuof dâ grôz riuwen.
alle die dâ wâren
die begunden sô gebâren,
als ein ingesinde guot
umbe ir lieben herren tuot.　　　　　　230
　　Als er diu kint weinen sach,
ze sînem sun er dô sprach:
'sun, war umbe weinestû ?
jâ gevellet dir nû
mîn lant und michel êre.
jâ vürhte ich harte sêre
dîner schœnen swester.

When he beheld his warriors true,   200
Blood relatives, and vassals tested,
His eyes upon his children rested.
Such great likeness could be seen
Betwen the two in form and mien,
Such wondrous beauty did they own,
A woman with a heart of stone
Would have rejoiced, and at their sight
She would have laughed with sheer delight.
Yet as their father saw the twain
His heart felt bitter, grievous pain.   210
He felt the anguish in him rise;
The tears welled up within his eyes
And fell upon his bed of state.
He said, "All help is now too late.
I must from you and this world fare.
I could now have begun to share
All joys with you and had delight
In growing old, with you in sight.
That solace now has taken flight,
Because Death holds me in his might."   220
   He gave the children with his hands
Unto the nobles of his lands
Who had assembled at his word.
Loud was the weeping to be heard.
The sobs that shook the children both
While loyal vassals took their oath
Made sorrow greater, and all grieved
As do true followers bereaved,
Through such bitter, sore disaster,
Of a well-beloved master.   230
   Seeing how the children cried,
He said, as he his young son eyed:
"My son, what cause have you to weep?
Verily now into your keep
Fall my great honor, realm, and power.
I greatly fear* at this sore hour
For your sister who's so fair.

des ist mîn jâmer vester
und beginnez nû ze spâte klagen
daz ich zallen mînen tagen   240
ir dinc niht baz geschaffet hân:
daz ist unväterlich getân.'

Er nam si beidiu bî der hant,
er sprach: 'sun, nû wis gemant
daz dû behaltest mêre
die jungisten lêre
die dir dîn vater tæte.
wis getriuwe, wis stæte,
wis milte, wis diemüete,
wis vrävele mit güete,   250
wis dîner zuht wol behuot,
den herren starc, den armen guot.
die dînen soltû êren,
die vremeden zuo dir kêren.
wis den wîsen gerne bî,
vliuch den tumben swâ er sî.
vor allen dingen minne got,
rihte wol durch sîn gebot.
ich bevilhe dir die sêle mîn
und diz schœne kint, die swester dîn,   260
daz dû dich wol an ir bewarst
und ir bruoderlîchen mite varst:
sô geschiht iu beiden wol.
got dem ich erbarmen sol
der geruoche iuwer beider phlegen.'
hie mite was ouch im gelegen
diu sprâche und des herzen kraft
und schiet sich diu geselleschaft,
beidiu sêle unde lîp.
hie weinden man unde wîp.   270
ein solhe bivilde er nam,
sôz landes herren wol gezam.

This grief keeps growing, that I bear;
And now too late I must lament
That I have not more wisely spent   240
My days in planning for her good.
I did not do what a father should."
   Their hands he held in his entwined:
"Remember, son," he said, "to mind
Forever these last words of mine.
To this advice your ear incline
That now your father gives to you:
Be loyal, steadfast, and be true:
Be charitable and devout;
Be fearless, yet be not without   250
A gentleness. Guard your good breeding:
Give to the poor; be unconceding
To nobles. Honor kith and kin,
And to your cause the stranger win;
Frequent the wise man willingly,
And flee the fool wherever he be.
First love God, and with just hand
Rule men because of God's command.
My soul I now to you commend
And bid you this fair child befriend—   260
Your sister cherish as you should,
Protecting her in brotherhood.
Then with the two of you it will
Fare well. May God Whose mercy still
Be mine, have care for both of you."
And then the power of speech withdrew
From him, and all his heart's strength fled.
His body and his soul, once wed,
Now parted company. And men
And women wept aloud again.   270
His obsequies were in accord
With what is due a sovereign lord.

Nû daz disiu rîchiu kint
sus beidenthalp verweiset sint,
der juncherre sich underwant
sîner swester dâ zehant
und phlac ir so er beste mohte,
als sînen triuwen tohte.
er volzôch ir muote
mit lîbe und mit guote,   280
si enwart von im beswæret nie.
er phlac ir sô (ich sagę iu wie)
daz er si nihts entwerte
swes si an in gerte
von kleidern und von gemache.
si wâren aller sache
gesellic und gemeine,
si wâren selten eine,
si wonden zallen zîten
einander bî sîten   290
(daz gezam vil wol in beiden),
si wâren ungescheiden
ze tische und ouch anderswâ.
ir bette stuonden alsô nâ
daz si sich mohten undersehen.
man enmac im anders niht gejehen,
er enphlægę ir alsô wol
als ein getriuwer bruoder sol
sîner lieben swester.
noch was diu liebe vester   300
die si im dâ wider truoc.
wünne heten si genuoc.
    Dô dise wünnę und den gemach
der werlde vîent ersach,
der durch hôchvart und durch nît

The orphaned brother and sister, in their devotion to one another, are led on by the Devil to incest. They grow fearful for their souls and for the fruit of their love.

Now that these children nobly born
Were thus left orphaned and forlorn,
The youth assumed without delay
His sister's care in every way
He could, and gave her his protection
Through sense of duty and affection.
He gratified her every whim,
Fulfilling all she asked of him.   280
Never did he grieve her now.
He cherished her (I'll tell you how)
By always serving her desire,
By granting all she might require
For her adornment, comfort, cheer.
     In all they were companions dear,
To one another dedicated;
Rarely were they separated,
But they continued to abide
Together always side by side;   290
(Proper for them both was that);
At table they together sat
And elsewhere never parted ways.
They slept so close that they could gaze
At one another from bed to bed.
It can not otherwise be said
Of him than that he took such good
And loving care of her as should
A brother of a sister dear.
For him she bore a love sincere,   300
Surpassing his by far. They knew
Delights and pleasures not a few.
     But when Creation's Foe caught sight
Of their great comfort and delight—
The Fiend, who lies sealed fast in Hell

versigelt in der helle lît,
ir beider êren in verdrôz
(wan si dûhte̦ in alze grôz)
und erzeicte sîn gewonheit:
wan im was ie und ist noch leit   310
swâ iemen dehein guot geschiht,
und enhenget sîn niht
swâ erz mac erwenden.
sus gedâhte er si phenden
ir vreuden und ir êren,
ob er möhte verkêren
ir vreude̦ ûf ungewinne.
an sîner swester minne
sô riet er im ze verre
unz daz der juncherre   320
verkêrte sîne triuwe guot
ûf einen valschen muot.

    Daz eine was diu minne
diu im verriet die sinne,
daz ander sîner swester schœne,
daz dritte stiuvels hœne,
daz vierde was sîn kintheit
diu ûf in mit dem tiuvel streit
unz er in dar ûf brâhte
daz er benamen gedâhte   330
mit sîner swester slâfen.
wâfen, herre, wâfen
über des hellehundes list,
daz er uns sô geværic ist!
war umbe verhenget im des got
daz er sô manigen grôzen spot
vrumet über sîn hantgetât
die er nâch im gebildet hât?

    Dô er durch des tiuvels rât
dise grôze missetât   340
sich ze tuonne bewac,
beidiu naht unde tac
wonde̦ er ir vriuntlîcher mite

Through arrogance and envy fell—
The honor shown them tried him hard
(He thought them paid too high regard),
And made him act as he always does;
For he is rueful, and ever was,   310
When fortune comes to any man;
And he will try as best he can
To turn man's happiness askew.
And so he planned to rob the two
Of both their honor and their bliss
By making pleasure go amiss,
Perverting all their joy to harm.
And so the Fiend employed the charm
Of the sister to excite
The youth with wicked appetite   320
Till he succumbed to Satan's lure
And wholesome love became impure.
    First concupiscence* showed the way
And led his senses all astray.
Then by her beauty he was stirred.
The Devil's insolence was third.*
Fourth, his childlishness allied
Itself against him on the side
Of Satan, till at length he brought
Him actually to the thought   330
Of sleeping with his sister. Oh!
Alas, O Lord, alas, oh woe!
How crafty is Hell's serpent vile,
To snare us so with cunning guile!
Oh, why does God so frequently
Allow the Devil's mockery
And let him vent his awful scorn
On man in God's own image born?
    Since to the Devil he paid heed,
Determined to commit this deed   340
Of wickedness, both night and day
He treated her in every way
As if he set far greater store

danne ê wære sîn site.
nû was daz einvalte kint
an sô getâner minne blint
und diu reine tumbe
enweste niht dar umbe
wes si sich hüeten solde
und hanctę im swes er wolde.   350
nû begap si der tiuvel nie
unz sîn willę an in ergie.

   Nû vristę erz unz an eine naht
dô mit slâfe was bedaht
diu juncvrouwe dâ si lac.
ir bruoder slâfes niht enphlac:
ûf stuont der unwîse
und sleich vil harte lîse
zuo ir bette dâ er si vant
unde huop daz ober gewant   360
ûf mit solhen sinnen
daz sis nie wart innen
unz er dar under zuo ir kam
und si an sînen arm genam.
ouwî waz woldę er drunder?
jâ lægę er baz besunder.
ez wâren von in beiden
diu kleider gescheiden
unz an daz declachen.
dô si begunde wachen,   370
dô hetę er si umbevangen.
ir munt und ir wangen
vant si sô gelîmet ligen
als dâ der tiuvel wil gesigen.

   Nû begunde er si triuten
mê danne vor den liuten
dâ vor wære sîn site.
hie verstuont si sich mite
daz ez ein ernest solde sîn.
si sprach: 'wie nû, bruoder mîn?   380
wes wiltû beginnen?

By her than he had done before.
The simple child could not surmise
What love appeared in such a guise;
Nor did the foolish virgin know
What she had better not bestow.
Not knowing what to keep from him,
She granted him his every whim.   350
    Meanwhile the Devil held his sway
Until with both he had his way.
Then he delayed his action till
One night the maiden lay quite still
And slumbered fast in deep repose.
Her brother did not sleep, but rose,
The foolish lad, and made his way
With stealthy step to where she lay
Upon her bed, and with great care
He softly raised the cover there   360
So cautiously that she remained
All unaware until he gained
Her side and took her, to her harm,
Beneath the sheet upon his arm.
Alas, the thing he willed at heart!
Far better that he lay apart!
Nothing on them did they wear;
The fallen covers left them bare
Save that one sheet bedecked the two.
As from sleep awake she grew,   370
He held her fast in his embrace,
Her lips and cheek pressed to his face.
Thus the Devil plays his game
When he the victory means to claim.
More than his wont in the eyes of men
The brother showed his love, and then
Grew intimate in fond caress.
    Now she perceived to her distress
That his behavior was no sport.
"O, brother mine," was her retort,   380
"What is it that you mean to do?

lâ dich von dînen sinnen
den tiuvel niht bringen.
waz diutet diz ringen ?'
si gedâhte: 'swîge ich stille,
so ergât des tiuvels wille
und wirde mînes bruoder brût,
unde wirde ich aber lût,
sô habe wir iemer mêre
verloren unser êre.'　　　　　　　　　　　　390
alsus versûmte si der gedanc,
unz daz er mit ir geranc,
wan er was starc und si ze kranc,
daz erz âne der guoten danc
brâhte ûf ein endespil.
dâ was der triuwen alze vil.
dar nâch beleip ez âne braht.
alsus wart si der selben naht
swanger bî ir bruoder.
der tiuvelschünde luoder　　　　　　　　　400
begunde si mêre schünden,
daz in mit den sünden
lieben begunde.
si hâlenz ûf die stunde
daz sich diu vrouwe des entstuont,
sô diu wîp vil schiere tuont,
daz si swanger wære.
dô wart ir vreude swære,
wanz enstiurte si niht ze huote:
si schein in unmuote.　　　　　　　　　　410
　　In geschach diu geswîche
von grôzer heimlîche:
heten si der entwichen,
sô wæren si unbeswichen.
nû sî gewarnet dar an
ein iegelîche man
daz er swester und niftel sî
niht ze heimlîche bî:
ez reizetz ungevüere

Don't let the Devil and his crew
Deprive you of your wits. What aim
Or meaning has this wrestling game?"
"If I keep silent," thought the lass,
"The Devil's wish will come to pass,
And I'll become my brother's bride.
But if I shout aloud and chide
We shall have lost forever more
All fame and honor that we bore."   390
Her thoughts kept her from calling out;
Vainly she grappled in this bout—
She was too weak and he was strong—
The wrestling game he did prolong
Against her will to see it through.
Devotion went beyond its due.
There was no cry and all was still.
    That night her brother had his will,
And she grew gravid with his child.
Tempted further and beguiled   400
By Satan's bait of such appeal,
They yielded and began to feel
Pleasure in their sinful way.
They concealed it till the day
When the youthful mistress knew,
As women know without ado,
That in her stirred her brother's seed.
Then all her joy was pain indeed.
In vain she struggled to conceal it.
Her sorrow served but to reveal it.   410
Their intimacy in excess
Deluded them to their distress.
Had they refrained from close embrace
They would have suffered no disgrace.
    Let their example serve to warn
Every man of woman born
Against his growing intimate
With female kin beyond what's fit.
Closeness that is such a snare

daz man wol verswüere.   420
    Alsô der junge
solhe wandelunge
an sîner swester gesach,
er nam si sunder unde sprach:
'vil liebiu swester, sage mir,
dû truobest sô, waz wirret dir?
ich hân an dir genomen war,
dû schînest harte riuwevar:
des was ich an dir ungewon.'
nû begunde si dâ von   430
siuften von herzen.
den angestlîchen smerzen
erzeicte si mit den ougen.
si sprach: 'des ist unlougen,
mir engê trûrennes nôt.
bruoder, ich bin zwir tôt,
an der sêle und an dem lîbe.
ouwê mir armen wîbe,
war zuo wart ich geborn?
wande ich hân durch dich verlorn   440
got und ouch die liute.
daz mein daz wir unz hiute
der werlde haben vor verstoln
daz enwil niht mêre sîn verholn.
ich bewar vil wol daz ich ez sage:
aber daz kint daz ich hie trage
daz tuot ez wol den liuten kunt.'
nû half der bruoder dâ zestunt
trûren sîner swester:
sîn jâmer wart noch vester.   450
    An disem ungewinne
erzeicte ouch vrou Minne
ir swære gewonheit:
si machet ie nâch liebe leit.
alsam ist in erwallen
daz honec mit der gallen.
er begunde sêre weinen,

It were better to forswear! 420
   The youthful ruler, when at last
He perceived her altered cast,
To one side his sister led
And in private to her said,
"Dearest sister, tell me true—
You are so grieved; what troubles you?
I have been watching you of late;
You seem in such a rueful state.
I am not used to that in you."
His words made her begin anew 430
To draw deep sighs with all her heart.
Her eyes betrayed her bitter smart
As she through heavy tears replied,
"It surely can not be denied
That I have cause to grieve and sigh:
For twofold is the death I die.
My flesh will perish, and my soul too.
Brother, alas, what can I do!
Unhappy me! Why was I born?
Because of you I am forlorn: 440
I've lost men's favor and God's grace.
How we have sinned in our embrace,
That till this day we've not revealed,
Can no longer be concealed.
My tongue I will guard cautiously,
Yet will the child I bear in me
Make manifest to all our sin."
Then the brother did begin
To sorrow with his sister, too;
And his grief yet stronger grew. 450
   Now Mistress Love made evident
In this calamity her bent.
She is one who would as lief
Let love always give way to grief.
In their love too it did befall
That with the honey mingled gall.
Sorely the young sovereign wept

daz houbet underleinen
sô riuweclichen mit der hant
als dem ze sorgen ist gewant.   460
ez stuont umbẹ al sîn êre:
iedoch sô klagetẹ er mêre
sîner swester arbeit
danne sîn selbes leit.

   Diu swester sach ir bruoder an,
si sprach: 'gehabe dich als ein man,
lâ dîn wîplich weinen stân
(ez enmac uns leider niht vervân)
und vint uns etelîchen rât,
ob wir durch unser missetât   470
âne gotes hulde müezen sîn,
daz doch unser kindelîn
mit uns iht verloren sî,
daz der vallẹ iht werden drî.
ouch ist uns ofte vor geseit
daz ein kint niene treit
sînes vater schulde.
ja ensol ez gotes hulde
niht dâ mite hân verlorn,
ob wir zer helle sîn geborn,   480
wandez an unser missetât
deheiner slahte schulde hât.'

   Nu begunde sîn herze wanken
in manigen gedanken.
ein wîlẹ er swîgende saz.
er sprach: 'swester, gehabe dich baz.
ich hân uns vunden einen rât
der uns ze staten gestât
ze verhelne unser schande.
ich hân in mînem lande   490
einen harte wîsen man

As he in bitter anguish kept
His brow pressed to his hand, forlorn,
Like one whose lot it is to mourn.   460
All his honor was at stake:
Yet he lamented more the ache
And suffering* his sister felt
Than the pain he had been dealt.
   His sister looked at him. "Be brave,"
She said, "and like a man behave.
Cease your woman's tears (alas,
They'll not avail in such a pass);
But find some help for us that we—
Without God's favor though we'll be,   470
Because we have so greatly erred—
May keep our child from being third
To suffer through our fall from grace,
That it at least may see God's face.
Often, too, we've heard declare*
That children do not ever bear
Their father's guilt. Indeed our child
Shall not forgo God's grace, defiled
Though we may be and born for Hell.
Yet it need not be damned as well;   480
For in our sin it has no share,
And guilt therefrom it does not bear."

    They decide to ask the advice of an old friend of
    their father, a wise counselor.

   He sat a while, torn in his mind,
And, swayed by thoughts of every kind,
At first no word to her did voice.
"Be cheered, dear sister, and rejoice!
This timely thought has come to me,"
He said at length, "that well may be
A way to help us hide our shame.
Within this wide realm that I claim   490
There is a man, extremely wise,

der uns wol gerâten kan,
den mir mîn vater ouch beschiet
und mir an sîne lêre riet,
dô er an sînem tôde lac,
wandę er ouch sînes râtes phlac.
den neme wir an unsern rât
(ich weiz wol daz er triuwe hât)
und volge wir sîner lêre:
sô gestât unser êre.'   500
   Diu vrouwe wart des râtes vrô.
ir vreude schuof sich alsô,
als ez ir dô was gewant:
ir enwas kein ganziu vreudę erkant.
daz ir trûren wære,
dô si was âne swære,
daz was ir bestiu vreude hie,
daz si niuwan ir weinen lie.
der rât behagetę ir harte wol,
si sprach: 'der uns dâ râten sol,   510
bruoder, den besendę enzît,
wan mîn tac unverre lît.'
   Nû wart er schiere besant:
der bote brâhte in zehant.
nû wart er schônę emphangen:
besunder wart gegangen
in eine kemenâten,
dâ si in râtes bâten.
alsus sprach der jungelinc:
'ich enhân umbe swachiu dinc   520
dich niht dâ her besant.
ich enweiz nû nieman der mîn lant
ze disen zîten bûwe,
dem ich sô wol getrûwe.
sît dich got sô gêret hât
(er gap dir triuwę und hôhen rât),
des lâ uns geniezen.
wir wellen dir entsliezen
ein heimlîche sache

A man well able to advise;
My father, as his death impended,
This very man to me commended,
And bade me his wise counsel heed,
As had been his own wont in need.
With him let us take counsel now
(For his discretion I avow);
As he directs, let us behave,
And thus our honor we shall save."   500
The young mistress at thought of aid
Rejoiced; yet joy in her but played
A role commensurate with her plight;
Joy unalloyed had taken flight.
What would have been of pain and grief*
While she was carefree, brought relief;
That she her tears could now suppress
Was her greatest happiness.
Gaining comfort from his plan,
"Brother," she said, "send for the man   510
At once to give us counsel here,
For my confinement day is near."*
    A herald summoned him straightway
And brought him back without delay.
A fitting welcome he was shown.
Then was he with the two alone
Into a heated chamber* brought
Where they his aid and counsel sought.
These words the youth addressed to him:
"It was no trivial thing or whim   520
That caused my summoning you here,
At my command thus to appear.
Of all that now in my realm dwell
I know no one I trust so well.
Since God has favored you with rare
Discernment and devotion, share
These gifts with us. We now propose
A secret matter to disclose—
A matter of such bitter shame,

diu uns nâch ungemache   530
umbẹ alle unser êre stât,
ez ensî daz uns dîn rât
durch got dâ von gescheide.'
sus buten si sich beide
weinendẹ ûf sînen vuoz.
er sprach: 'herre, dirre gruoz
der diuhte mich ze grôz,
wærẹ ich joch iuwer genôz.
stât ûf, herre, durch got,
lât hœren iuwer gebot   540
daz ich niemer zebrechen wil
und gebet dirre redẹ ein zil.
saget mir waz iu werre.
ir sît mîn geborner herre:
ich râtẹ iu sô ich beste kan,
dâ engezwîvelt niemer an.'
    Nû tâten sị im ir sache kunt.
er half in beiden dâ ze stunt
weinen vor leide
(er meinde wol si beide)   550
und trôste si vil harte wol,
sô man den vriunt nâch leide sol
daz nieman doch erwenden kan.
sus sprach daz kint zem wîsen man:
'herre, nu vint uns einen rât
der uns nû aller nâhest gât,
sô uns nû kumet diu zît
daz mîn swester gelît,
wâ si des kindes genese
daz ir geburt verswigen wese.   560
nû gedenkẹ ich, ob ich wone
die wîle mîner swester vone
ûzerhalp dem lande,
daz unser zweier schande
sî verswigen deste baz.'

We'll lose all honor and good name   530
Save by God's grace you give us aid
Impending ruin to evade."
At his feet the children kneeled
And through their tears to him appealed.
   Thereupon the noble said,
"My lord, if I were born and bred
Your peer, too much you'd condescend
To greet me thus and to extend
Such deference. My lord, do stand,
In heaven's name; speak your command   540
That I will never disobey;
And say what it is you must say.
What troubles you, make known to me.
You are my lord by birth's decree;
Never doubt that this holds true:
As best I can I'll counsel you."
   Sadly weeping, they revealed
What till now they had concealed.
He wept with them in their dejection
(For both of them he felt affection);   550
He gave them comfort and relief
As one should comfort friends in grief
To which they must grow reconciled.
Then to the wise man said the child:
"Sir, help us that we may succeed
In finding what we now most need.
When the day and hour draw nigh
And in childbirth she must lie,
Where can my sister be confined
To keep it hidden from mankind?   560
Now I have thought it might be well
If during this time I should dwell
Far from my sister and this place,
Beyond my realm, that our disgrace
May be the better hid from view."

Der wîse sprach: 'sô râtę ich daz:
die iuwers landes walten,
die jungen zuo den alten,
sult ir ze hove gebieten
und die iuwerm vater rieten.   570
ir sult iuch wider si enbarn
daz ir zehant wellet varn
durch got zem heiligen grabe.
mit bete gewinnet uns abe
daz wir der vrouwen hulde swern
(des beginnet sich dâ nieman wern),
daz si des landes müeze phlegen
unz ir belîbet under wegen.
dâ büezet iuwer sünde
als iuch des got geschünde.   580
der lîp hât wider in getân:
den lât im ouch ze buoze stân.
und begrîfet iuch dâ der tôt,
sô ist des eides harte nôt
daz si unser vrouwe müeze sîn.
bevelhet si ûf die triuwe mîn
vor den herren allen:
daz muoz in wol gevallen,
wandę ich der altistę under in
und ouch der rîchiste bin.   590
sô nim ich si hin heim ze mir:
solhen gemach schaffę ich ir
daz si daz kint alsô gebirt
daz des nieman innen wirt.
got gesendę iuch wider, herre:
des getrûwę ich im vil verre.
belîbet ir dannę under wegen,
so gevallet iu der gotes segen.
zewâre sô enist niht mîn rât
daz si durch dise missetât   600

The counselor gives them advice which they
heed.

"This is my advice to you,"
The wise man said. "To court command
The foremost leaders of your land,
Both young and old, that they appear;
And bid your father's counselors here.   570
Then to them all you should unfold
Your wish as pilgrim to behold
For God's dear sake the Holy Grave.
Allegiance to our mistress crave,
And pray we pledge it her by oath
(To do this no one will be loath)
That she shall rule without gainsay
So long as you remain away.
On your crusade then penitent,
As God directs you, there repent.   580
Your body sinned against Him; let
Your body do Him penance. Yet
If there to death you must submit,
The oath will be most requisite
That she be our liege lady then.
Before the gathered noblemen
Entrust her to my loyal care;
Since I am both the oldest there
And of them all the mightiest,
It should well satisfy the rest.   590
Thus shall I take her home to me
And furnish her with quarters free
From prying eyes, that she may bear
The child, and no one be aware.
May God send you home, my lord;
I trust all this to His accord.
If on your way your days you end,
God's blessing will on you descend.
    But for your sister's sin I'd say
She ought not to repent this way;   600

der werlde iht emphliehe,
des landes sich entziehe.
belîbet si bî dem lande,
ir sünde und ir schande
mac si sô baz gebüezen.
si mac den armen grüezen
mit guote und mit muote,
bestât si bî dem guote.
gebristet ir des guotes,
so enhât si niht wans muotes:　　　　　　610
nû waz mac danne ir muot
gevrumen ieman âne guot?
waz touc der muot âne guot
oder guot âne muot?
ein teil vrumet muot âne guot,
noch bezzer ist guot unde muot.
von diu sô dunket mich daz guot,
si behabe guot unde muot:
sô mac si mit dem guote
volziehen dem muote,　　　　　　　620
sô rihte gote mit muote,
mit lîbe und mit guote.
ouch râte ich iu den selben muot.'
der rât dûhte si beide guot
und volgeten alsô drâte
sînem guoten râte.
　Dô die herren überz lant
ze hove wurden besant,
dô si vür kâmen
und ir herren vernâmen,　　　　　　630
sîner bete wart gevolget sâ.
dem alten bevalh er dâ
sîne swester bî der hant.
sus gedâhte er rûmen sîn lant.
den schaz den in ir vater lie,
der wart mit ir geteilet hie.
　Sus schieden si sich beide
mit grôzem herzeleide.

She should within the world remain
And not renounce her own domain.
If she holds to the realm and stays
She will atone in better ways
For her disgrace and sin. Indeed,
The poor she can assure in need,
Assisting them materially
If she retains her property.
   But if of wealth she has no fill,*
She will have nothing but good will.   610
What good to them is her good will
If she lacks means their needs to fill?
Without wealth how can good will fill
Men's wants, or wealth without good will?
Good will alone does some needs fill,
But better both wealth and good will.
And so I think, her need to fill,
She should keep both, wealth and good will.
Thus with her wealth she can fulfil
The dictates of her own good will,   620
To God atoning to her fill
With wealth, her person, and good will.
You, too, I urge to bear good will."
Straightway they hastened to fulfil
His counsel, for both felt at heart
That his advice was wisdom's part.
   Now when the lords from all the land
Appeared at court upon command
And heard in full assembly there
What their liege lord had to declare,   630
They straightway granted him his plea.
His sister he then personally
Placed in the aged counselor's hands.
And so he planned to leave his lands.
He shared with her his father's treasure,
Dividing it in fitting measure.
So came the time when they both parted,
Each from the other, heavy hearted.

enheten si niht gevürhtet got,
si heten iemer der werlde spot   640
geduldet vür daz scheiden.
man möhte von in beiden
dâ grôzen jâmer hân gesehen.
niemer müeze mir geschehen
alsô grôzer ungemach,
als den gelieben geschach,
dô si sich muosen scheiden.
zewârę ez was in beiden
diu vreude alsô tiure
sam daz îs dem viure.   650
ein getriuwiu wandelungę ergie,
dô si sich muosen scheiden hie:
sîn herze volgetę ir von dan,
daz ir bestuont bî dem man.
durch nôt tet in daz scheiden wê:
si engesâhen ein ander niemer mê.

    Nû vuorte dirre wîse man
sîne juncvrouwen dan
in sîn hûs, dâ ir geschach
michel guot und gemach.   660
nû was sîn hûsvrouwę ein wip
diu beidiu sinne unde lîp
in gotes dienest hâtę ergeben:
dehein wîp endorfte bezzer leben.
diu half in ânę untriuwe steln,
ir vrouwen kumber verheln,
sô wîbes güete gezam,
daz ir geburt sô ende nam
daz der nieman wart gewar.
ez was ein sun daz si gebar,   670
der guote sündære

Had they not feared God's reprimand
They would have chosen to withstand   640
The world's reproach rather than part.
One could see in each one's heart
How deep the sorrow and how great!
May it never be my fate
To suffer such unhappiness
As these two lovers through duress
Of parting had to undergo.
What joy was there that they could know?
Joy they could no more have felt
Than could ice in fire not melt.   650
When they were forced to leave each other
Their hearts exchanged with one another:
He left, but left his heart to stay;
She stayed, but her heart went his way.
They had to part; their grief was sore.
They saw each other never more.

    A son is born, secretly placed in a small bark,
and exposed on the sea. An inscribed tablet
accompanies the child.

Now when the counselor in turn
Brought his liege lady to sojourn
At his house, she was given there
Kindness, comfort, and great care.   660
The nature of the counselor's wife
Was such that she had spent her life
Serving God with body and mind;
A better woman one could not find.
Devotedly she helped conceal,
With kind and fitting womanly zeal,
Their lady's sad predicament.
So hidden was the whole event
That none else knew of it on earth.
To a son she there gave birth.   670
The good sinner* was that son

von dem disiu mære
von allerêrstẹ erhaben sint.
ez was ein wünneclîchez kint.
zes kindes gebürte
was niemen zantwürte
niuwan dise vrouwen zwô.
der wirt wart dar geladet dô:
und als er daz kint ersach,
mit den vrouwen er des jach   680
daz nie zer werlde kæme
ein kint alsô genæme.
  Nû wurden sị alsô drâte
under in ze râte
wiez verholen möhte sîn.
si sprâchen, diz schœne kindelîn
daz wære schedelich verlorn:
nû wære aber ez geborn
mit alsô grôzen sünden,
ez enwoldẹ in got künden,   690
daz si niene westen
von ræten den besten.
an got sazten si den rât,
daz er si aller untât
bewartẹ an disen dingen.
dô muosẹ in wol gelingen,
wan im niemer missegât
der sich ze rehtẹ an in verlât.
  Nû kam in vaste in den muot,
in enwære niht sô guot   700
so daz siz versanden ûf den sê.
daz wart niht gevristet mê:
der wirt huop sich verstolne
und gewan vil verholne
ein väzzelîn vil veste
und hie zuo daz beste
daz deheinez möhte sîn.
dâ wart daz schœne kindelîn
mit manigem trahen in geleit,

Of whom this tale was first begun.
The little child whom she did bear
Was wondrous sweet beyond compare.
While the liege lady was confined
No one else of all mankind
Was present save these women two.
The lord was summoned there to view
The little child, and then indeed
With both the women he agreed   680
That never had a child been seen
So pleasing both in form and mien.

    Together they, without delay,
Deliberated in what way*
The child could be concealed. "Oh, why,"
They said, "should this sweet infant die?
That would be a calamity."
What course to take they could not see—
For it was born in such great sin,
They did not know where to begin   690
Save God to them make manifest
What procedure would be best.
These matters they placed in God's hand
So that their ways He might command
And from all error set them free.
They could not but successful be,
For he will never go astray
Who trusts God in the proper way.

    Now it struck their minds with force
That they could take no better course*   700
Than to send the child away
By sea. There was no more delay.
The master then in secrecy
Set out and surreptitiously
Obtained a small but sturdy chest,
For this purpose by far the best
That could be found. Into its keeping
The lovely child, amidst great weeping,
Was placed, with costly silks, spread under

under unde über gespreit   710
alsô rîchiu sîdîn wât
daz nieman bezzere hât.
ouch wurden zuo im dar in
geleit, als ich bewîset bin,
zweinzic marke von golde,
dâ mite man ez solde
ziehen obz ze lande
got iemer gesande.

   Ein tavel wart getragen dar
der vrouwen diu daz kint gebar   720
diu vil guot helfenbein was,
gezieret wol, als ich ez las,
von golde und von gesteine,
daz ich nie deheine
alsô guote gewan.
dâ schreip diu muoter an
sô si meiste mahte
von des kindes ahte:
wan si hâte des gedingen
daz ez got solde bringen   730
den liuten ze handen
die got an im erkanden.

   Dar an stuont geschriben sô:
ez wære von gebürte hô,
unde diuz gebære
daz diu sîn base wære,
sîn vater wære sîn œhein,
ez wære, ze helne daz mein,
versendet ûf den sê.
dannoch schreip si mê: 740
daz manz toufen solde
und ziehen mit dem golde,
und ob sîn vindære
alsô kristen wære,
daz er im den schaz mêrte
undz ouch diu buoch lêrte,
sîn tavel im behielte

And above him, of such wonder, 710
Fabrics so precious and so rare,
There are none better anywhere.
In the chest, as I've been told,
Twenty marks of purest gold
Were likewise placed beside the boy
As means the finder could employ
To rear the child, if God so planned
To let it safely come to land.

They brought a tablet of great worth
To her who gave the child its birth. 720
This tablet, as I've read, was made
Of finest ivory, inlaid
With gold and gems without a flaw,
The like of which I never saw.
The mother on the tablet wrote
As much as she could to denote
The infant's rank and to review
All the circumstances, too.
She felt great hope: God would provide
The infant with due care, and guide 730
Its course to men who God revere,
Who for His sake the child would rear.

The writing on the tablet said:
The child had been most nobly bred.*
She who bore him, as it befell,
Was his mother and aunt as well;
His father was his uncle too.
To hide this sinful love from view,
The newborn babe had been exposed
Upon the sea. She then disclosed 740
Her wish to have the child baptized,
The gold to rear it utilized.
And, should the finder wish to be
Truly a Christian, he would see
To it that the child's treasure grew;
And let him learn the Scriptures* too;
And keep the tablet and take care

und im der schrift wielte,
würdez iemer ze man,
daz er læse daran   750
alle dise geschiht,
sô überhüebe er sich niht,
unde würde er alsô guot
daz er ze gote sînen muot
wenden begunde,
sô buozte er zaller stunde
durch sîner triuwen rât
sînes vater missetât,
und daz er ouch der gedæhte
diu in zer werlde bræhte: 760
des wære in beiden nôt
vür den êwigen tôt.
im wart dâ niht benant
weder liute noch lant,
geburt noch sîn heimuot:
daz was ouch in ze helne guot.
    Dô der brief was gereit,
dô wart diu tavele geleit
zuo im in daz kleine vaz.
dô besluzzen si daz   770
mit solher gewarheit
daz deheiner slahte leit
geschæhe dem kinde
von regen noch von winde
noch von der ünden vreise
ûf der wazzerreise
ze zwein tagen oder ze drin.
alsus truogen si ez hin
bî der naht zuo dem sê:
vor dem tage enmohten si ê.   780
dâ vunden si eine barke
ledige unde starke:
dâ leiten si mit jâmer an
disen kleinen schefman.
dô sande im der süeze Krist

Of the inscription for him. There
The child could thus read of his fate,
If he should come to man's estate.   750
Then, having learned his history,
From arrogance he would be free;
And, if his virtue grew so great
That he would strive to dedicate
Himself to God, he would not shun
The loving duty of a son:
Atoning constantly* to win
Forgiveness for his father's sin.
Her, too, she hoped he'd bear in mind,
Who gave him birth among mankind.   760
Both needed his true penance, or
They might be damned forever more.
Unnamed was all his pedigree,
His nation, country, family,
And birthplace; for they felt they should
Keep these things secret for his good.
   When this in script had been expressed
She placed the tablet in the chest
Where the little baby lay.
Then such care did they display   770
As the tiny chest they closed
That to no harm it was exposed
If blown by wind, or struck by rain,
Or tossed by violence of the main
Upon its journey on the sea,
That well might last two days or three.
They waited then until the night,
For earlier, while it was light,
They dared not do what they had planned,
And bore it to the ocean's strand.   780
Upon the beach, there in the dark,
They found a strong and empty bark
And in it sorrowfully placed
The little skipper, fast incased.
Sweet Christ, Who is more than benign,

der bezzer danne gnædic ist
den vil rehten wunschwint:
si stiezen an, hin vlôz daz kint.

Ir wizzet wol daz ein man
der ir iewederz nie gewan,   790
reht liep noch grôzez herzeleit,
dem ist der munt niht sô gereit
rehte ze sprechenne dâ von
sô dem der ir ist gewon.
nû bin ich gescheiden
dâ zwischen von in beiden,
wan mir iewederz nie geschach:
ich engewan nie liep noch ungemach,
ich enlebe übele noch wol.
dâ von enmac ich als ich sol   800
der vrouwen leit entdecken
noch mit worten errecken,
wan ez wære von ir schaden
tûsent herze überladen.
Der beswærde wâren driu
diu diu vrouwe einiu
garwe an ir herzen truoc,
der iegelîcher wære genuoc
vil maniges wîbes herzen.
si truoc den einen smerzen   810
von dem meine daz si begie
mit ir bruoder den si lie.
der siechtuom der ander was,
daz si des kindes genas.
daz dritte was diu vorhte
die ir der jâmer worhte
nâch ir lieben kinde
daz si dem wilden winde

The fairest wind upon the brine
Let blow. They pushed the little boat,
And off it went with child afloat.

> The poet apologizes for his inability to describe
> the mother's grief upon the loss of both her child
> and her brother.

  This you know full well: he who
Has never felt a joy that's true,   790
Or a deep sorrow, will be less
Apt to find words to express
These feelings justly than will he
Who has felt both in full degree.
Now equally remote from me
Are both, for I was always free
Of them, since I have never felt
Great joy or deep distress.* Life dealt
Me neither evil nor great good.
I can not, therefore, as I should,   800
Convey or find words to depict
Her grief, so great it would afflict
A thousand hearts that all would be
Weighed down by such calamity.
  Three were the sorrows* she then felt
That life to her alone had dealt—
And she the mistress of a realm—
Each one enough to overwhelm
Many a heart of womankind.
She suffered first in heart and mind   810
Because she'd sinned with her own brother
And had to part, each from the other.
Secondly, she still was frail
And weak in body from travail.
And, thirdly, she was in a state
Of dread anxiety, so great
Her longing for her lovely child
That to the winds so rough and wild

hete bevolhen ûf den sê
und enweste niht, wiez im ergê, 820
wederz genæsę oder læge tôt.
si was geborn ze grôzer nôt.
noch enwas ez niht gescheiden
mit disen drin leiden.
unmanic tac ende nam
unz ir bœse mære kam
und der grœzist ungemach
der ir zir lebenę ie geschach,
daz ir bruoder wære tôt.
der tôt kam im von seneder nôt. 830

Dô si von ir bruoder schiet,
als in der wîse beiden riet,
nu begundę er siechen zehant
(des twanc in der minne bant)
und muose belîben sîner vart
der er durch got enein wart.
sîn jâmer wart sô vestęr
nâch sîner lieben swester
daz er ze deheiner stunde
sich getrœsten kunde. 840
alsus dorretę im der lîp.
swie si doch jehen daz diu wîp
sêrer minnen dan die man,
des enist niht, daz schein dar an:
wande sîn herzeleit
daz im was vür gespreit,
daz was dâ wider kleine,
niuwan diu minne eine
diu im ein zil des tôdes was:
der hete si vieriu und genas. 850
sus ergreif in diu senede nôt
und lac vor herzeriuwe tôt.

Diz mære wart ir kunt getân,
dô si ze kirchen solde gân,
rehte dâ vor drîer tage.
nû vuor si hin mit grôzer klage

She'd trusted on the sea, not knowing
What perils he was undergoing, 820
Whether he were saved or dead.
To suffer she was born and bred,
For these sorrows did not end
The woe that on her did descend;
Thus but a few days had she grieved
When evil tidings she received:
To death her brother had fallen thrall.
From this she suffered worst of all.

That from her he had had to part
Made longing for her break his heart. 830
No sooner had she gone away,
Acting on the wise man's say,
Than he at once began to languish
(Love's shackles bound him fast in anguish):
The journey planned for God's own sake
He could no longer undertake.
Increasing strong his yearning grew
For his dear sister, that he knew
No peace or comfort night or day:
His feeble frame wasted away. 840
Though it is said with confidence
That woman's love is more intense*
Than is a man's, it is not so,
As will what follows clearly show:
The suffering he faced was slight
Compared with what was her sad plight,
Save that his love was so intense,
Of such consuming violence,
It was for him the road to Death:
Her griefs were fourfold, yet Life's breath 850
She kept. But him Love's sickness plied
With hungry sting so that he died.*
She was informed of this new blow
Three days before she was to go
For churching.* Great was her lament
As she in grief and mourning* went

und begruop ir bruoder und ir man.
dô si daz lant zuo ir gewan

unde daz ze mære erschal
in den landen über al,   860
vil manic rîcher herre
nâhen unde verre
die gerten ir ze wîbe.
an gebürte und an lîbe,
an der rîcheit und an der jugent,
an der schœnę und an der tugent,
an zuht und an güete
und an allem ir gemüete
sô was si guotes mannes wert:
doch wurden si allę entwert.   870
   Si hete zuo ir minnę erwelt
weizgot einen starken helt,
den aller tiuristen man
der ie minne gewan.
vor dem zierte si ir lîp,
als ein minnendez wîp
ûf einen biderben man sol
dem si gerne behagete wol.
swie vastez sî wider dem site
daz dehein wîp mannes bite,   880
sô lac si im doch allez an,
sô si des state gewan,
mit dem herzen zaller stunde,
swie joch mit dem munde:
ich meine den gnædigen got.
sît daz ir des tiuvels spot
sîne hulde hetę entworht,
daz hete sị nû sô sêrę ervorht
daz si vreude und gemach

To the burial of him she knew
As brother and as husband, too.

> The youthful lady of the realm does penance.
> Her land is devastated by a duke whom she re-
> fuses to marry.

It came about when news was spread
Throughout the realm that he was dead   860
And she the ruler of the land:
Great lords a-plenty sought her hand
In marriage from afar and near.
Her rank and person, without peer,
Her vast possessions and her youth,
Her manner and her charm, in truth,
Her upbringing and gentleness,
Her character and whole address
Deserved a worthy man indeed.
Yet to no suitor paid she heed.   870
    As her love a Man she chose,
A mighty Hero,* Heaven knows,
A Man dearer than any man
Who has been loved since time began.
For Him her body she made sweet,
As for a loving wife is meet
Who wants to please and honor, too,
A husband who is good and true.
Though custom strongly has eschewed
That man by womankind be wooed,   880
She failed no opportunity,
However often that might be,
To court Him with each word and phrase.
Her heart sang always in His praise.
By Him I mean the Gracious Lord.
Since Satan's mockery had scored
And robbed her of God's grace so dear,
She had succumbed to such great fear
That to regain God's grace once more

durch sîne hulde versprach   890
sô daz si naht unde tac
solher unmuoze phlac
diu dem lîbe unsanfte tete.
beide mit wachen und mit gebete,
mit almuosen und mit vasten
enlie sin lîp nie gerasten.
diu wâre riuwe was dâ bî,
diu aller sünden machet vrî.

 Nû was ir ein herre
gesezzen unverre,   900
des namen ir vil wol gelîch,
beidiu edel unde rîch:
der leite sînen vlîz dar an
daz si in næme ze man.
und dô er sîn reht getete
mit boteschefte und mit bete
als erz versuochen solde
und si sîn niene wolde,
nû wânde er si gewinnen sô:
mit urliuge und mit drô   910
sô bestuont er si zehant
unde wuoste ir daz lant.
er gewan ir abe die besten
stete und ir vesten
unz er si garwe vertreip,
daz ir niht mê beleip
niuwan eine ir houbetstat.
diu was ouch alsô besat
mit tägelîcher huote,
ez enwelle got der guote   920
mit sînen gnâden understân,
si muoz ouch die verloren hân.

All joy and comfort she forswore.   890
And so she would both night and day
Chastise her body in such a way
That harsh pain she would have to bear.
Through fasting, vigils, and through prayer,
Through works of mercy without cease,
She never gave her body peace.
The true remorse she showed herein
Was that which frees man of all sin.
    There lived a lord not far away,
Of noble birth and mighty sway.   900
He was no less rich than she;
She bore no higher rank than he.
He persevered with might and main
Her hand in marriage to obtain.
When he had sued her as he should,
And done all that a suitor could
With messengers and formal plea,
And she refused him steadfastly,
Thus did he hope to win her then:
With threat, with warfare, with his men,   910
He attacked in swift campaign
And devastated her domain.
Each stronghold, every finest town,
He captured from her and tore down,
Till he so far had driven her
That in but one town could she stir,
The capital of her domain.
So beseiged did she remain,
So well beleaguered the citadel,
She would have lost this town as well   920
If through His grace God had not pleased
To prevent its being seized.

Nû lâzen dise rede hie
unde sagen wiez ergie
dirre vrouwen kinde
daz die wilden winde
wurfen swar in got gebôt,
in daz leben oder in den tôt.
unser herre got der guote
underwant sich sîn ze huote,   930
von des genâden Jônas
ouch in dem mere genas,
der drîe tagẹ und drîe naht
in dem wâge was bedaht
in eines visches wamme.
er was des kindes amme
unz daz erz gesande
wol gesunt ze lande.
    In zwein nehten und einem tage
kam ez von der ünden slage   940
zeinem einlande,
als ez got dar gesande.
ein klôster an dem stade lac,
des ein geistlich abbet phlac.
der gebôt zwein vischæren
daz si benamen wæren
vor tage vischen ûf den sê.
dô tet in daz weter wê:
der wintwarp alsô dôz

74

CHAPTER II

Gregorius and the Abbot

In a storm at sea, the child is rescued by fisher-men.

This story, that we now relate,
Let us halt to tell the fate
Of this liege lady's infant child
Whom the winds, so rough and wild,
Were tossing on to safety, or,
As God commanded, to death's shore.
Our Gracious Lord, Dear God so Fair,
Assumed the little infant's care,   930
As once He rescued Jonah, who
By His grace, was sheltered, too,
Amid the very waves at sea
For days and nights, in number three,
Within a fish's belly. Thus
God, the Lord so Bounteous,
Himself the child's Nurse was and fed it,
Till safely to the shore He sped it.
After two nights and a day,
Tossed by beating waves and spray,   940
The child came to an island strand,
Driven there by God's own hand.
    Near shore a monastery stood,
The abbot of this brotherhood,
A priest. Now he explicitly
Bade two fishers go to sea
And start their fishing before dawn.
The fishers into storm were drawn.
By thundering waves they were so splashed,

daz si kleine noch grôz 950
mohten gevâhen.
si begunden wider gâhen.
in der widerreise
vunden si ûf der vreise
sweben des kindes barke.
nû wunderte si vil starke
wie si dar komen wære
alsô liute lære.
si zugen dar zuo sô nâhen
daz si dar inne sâhen 960
ligen daz wênige vaz.
dar ûz huoben si daz
und leitenz in daz schef zuo in:
diu barke ran lære hin.
    Daz wintgestœze wart sô grôz
daz si ûf dem sê verdrôz.
diu state enmohte in niht geschehen
daz si hæten besehen
waz in dem vazze wære.
daz was in aber unmære: 970
wan si hâten des gedâht,
sô siz ze hûse hæten brâht,
so besæhen si mit gemache
ir vundene sache.
si wurfen drüber ir gewant
und zugen vaste an daz lant.
    Iemitten kuren si den tac.
der abbet der der zelle phlac
gie kurzwîlen zuo dem sê,
er alters eine und nieman mê, 980
und warte der vischære,
welh ir gelücke wære.
dô vuoren si enmitten zuo:
des dûhten abbet alze vruo.
er sprach: 'wie istz ergangen?
habet ir iht gevangen?'
si sprâchen 'lieber herre,

By violent winds so cruelly lashed,   950
They made no catch, not great nor small,
And turned back with no fish at all.
While they hurried, homeward bound,
Upon the seething sea they found)
The infant's little bark afloat.
Amazed at seeing such a boat,
They marveled that it was un-oared
And that it had no one aboard.
With their own craft they drew so near,
Into the bark they now could peer   960
And see the small chest lying there.
They placed it, raising it with care,
Into their boat. The empty bark
Floated off into the dark.

The tempest raged so violently
That they grew troubled on the sea.
Such was their precarious state,
They could not then investigate
The contents of the little chest;
By this they were no whit distressed,   970
For they had planned and had in mind
To open and inspect their find
At their convenience, leisurely,
Once they were home and off the sea.
They threw their gear upon it, and
Rapidly they rowed toward land.

Day broke as they were nearing shore.
The ruling abbot just before
Had left the abbey for a stroll
Along the beach, the only soul,   980
On lookout for the fishermen,
To see what luck was theirs. Just then
Their fishing craft to shore they brought.
By far too soon, the abbot thought,
Had they returned. "How did it go?
And have you any catch to show?"
He asked. "Dear master," they replied,

wir wâren alze verre
gevaren ûf den wilden sê.
uns wart von weter nie sô wê: 990
uns was der tôt vil nâch beschert,
wir haben den lîp vil kûmę ernert.'
er sprach: 'nû lât die vische wesen:
got lobę ich daz ir sît genesen
und alsô komen an daz stat.'
der abbet im dô sagen bat,
er sprach, waz ez möhte sîn:
dâ meinde er daz väzzelîn
daz mit dem gewande was gespreit.
diu vrâge was in beiden leit   1000
und sprâchen, wes ein herre
vrâgetę alsô verre
umbę armer liute sache
in beiden zungemache.
dô reichtę er dar mit dem stabe,
daz gewant warf er abe
und sach daz wênige vaz.
er sprach: 'wâ nâmet ir daz ?'
nû gedâhten sį maniger lügen,
wie si den abbet betrügen,   1010
und wolden imz entsaget hân
und hæten daz ouch wol getân,
wan daz ers wart innen
von unsers herren minnen.
Dô er die vrâge wolde lân
und wider in sîn klôster gân,
do erweindez kint vil lûte
und kunte dem gotes trûte
daz ez dâ wære.
dô sprach der gewære: 1020
'hie ist ein kint inne.
saget mir in der minne,
wâ habet irz genomen ?
wie istz iu zuo komen ?
daz wil ich wizzen, crêde mich.'

"Too far out our oars we plied.
Such fierce weather have we had,
Never before was storm so bad. 990
We narrowly escaped from death,
And by great effort kept the breath
Of life in us." Then said the priest,
"No matter about the fish! At least,
God be praised, you're here and well
And safe on shore." He bade them tell
What it was they had—he meant
The small chest that was evident
Beneath the gear spread over it.
    Unwelcome was so definite 1000
A question to both fishermen.
And of the abbot they asked then
Why a master questioned so,
To their chagrin, and had to know
All about poor men's affairs.
The abbot, at this talk of theirs,
With his staff thrust off the gear,
And saw the little chest appear.
"Now, where did you get this?" he asked.
The truth with many lies they masked. 1010
The knowledge of it they'd have kept
Successfully from him except
That suddenly he grew aware
Through God's own Love of what was there.
No more would he have questioned then
But to his cloister gone again
When loudly the small child cried out
And left the godly man no doubt
That it was lying hidden there.
    Then did the upright man declare: 1020
"There is a little child in here.
Tell me, by God's love so dear,
Where did you this child obtain?
How did you come by it? Explain!
Crede me,* this I must know."

dô bedâhten si sich
und sageten im als ich iu ê,
wie siz vunden ûf dem sê.
nû hiez erz heven ûf den sant
unde lœsen abe diu bant.   1030
dô sach er ligen dar inne
seltsæne gewinne,
ein kint, daz im sîn herze jach
daz er sô schœnez nie gesach.
    Der ellende weise,
wandę er deheine vreise
gevürhten niene kunde,
mit einem süezen munde
sô lachetę er den abbet an.

und alsô der gelêrte man   1040
an sîner tavele gelas
wie daz kint geboren was,
[daz manz noch toufen solde
und ziehen mit dem golde,]
daz kundę er wol verswîgen.
ze gote begundę er nîgen,
ze himele huop er tougen
die hende und diu ougen
und lobete got des vundes
und skindes gesundes.   1050
    Daz kindelîn si vunden
mit phelle bewunden,
geworht zAlexandrîe.
nû westenz dise drîe:
ez enwart ouch vürbaz niht gespreit.
ouch saget uns diu wârheit
von den vischæren

They bethought themselves, and so
Told him the tale told you by me,
Of how they'd found it out at sea.
He had them lift it to the sands
And bade them then remove the bands.   1030
He saw within the little chest
A strange haul lying manifest:
A child—so fair, so exquisite,
His heart confessed, none rivaled it.
The banished orphan child, since yet
Of fear, of danger, or of threat
It nothing knew, with lovely smile
Upon its sweet mouth without guile,
Laughed up into the abbot's face.

> The ruling abbot assumes the supervision of the
> child's upbringing and binds* the fishermen to
> secrecy about its discovery. He becomes the
> child's godfather and baptizes it in his own
> name, Gregorius.

The learned man, who, by God's grace,   1040
Had read what the small tablet said
Of how the child was born and bred
(The child should be baptized, it told,
And reared to manhood with the gold),
Could keep these matters well concealed.
First of all to God he kneeled.
With hands and eyes raised to the sky,
He silently* praised God on high
That the infant had been found
And had survived thus safe and sound.   1050
The little child that they had found,
In costly silks* was wrapped around,
Of Alexandrine weave and hue.
Of this alone these three men knew,
None else, nor was it further spread.
Now of these fishers it was said
That both the men were brothers—thus

daz si gebruoder wæren.
die muosen im beide
mit triuwen und mit eide 1060
vil wol bestæten daz,
si ensagetenz niemer vürbaz.
    Die bruoder wâren ungelîch,
der eine was arm, der ander rîch.
der arme bî dem klôster saz,
der rîche wol hin dan baz
wol über einer mîle zil.
der arme hete kinde vil:
der rîche nie dehein kint gewan,
niuwan ein tohter, diu hete man. 1070
nû wart der abbet enein
vil guoter vuoge mit den zwein,
daz sich der ermere man
næme daz kint an
und ez dâ nâhen bî im züge
und den liuten alsus lüge,
swer in ze deheiner stunde
vrâgen begunde
wâ er daz kint hete genomen,
daz ez im wære komen 1080
von sînes bruoder tohter
(deheinen list enmohter
erdenken sô gevüegen)
unde daz siz trüegen,
sô si wol enbizzen sît
unz nâch der messezît,
und man den abbet bæte
daz er sô wol tæte
undz kint selbe toufte
und dâ mite koufte 1090
got und ir dienesthaften muot.
der rât was gevüege und guot.
    Nû nam der abbet dâ den rât,
golt und die sîdîne wât,
und gap dem armen dô zehant

The true source of our tale tells us.
Under promise, under oath
To the abbot, then, they both   1060
Had firmly to asseverate
That this they never would relate.
   The brothers differed from one another;
The one was poor, and rich the other.
The poor man's dwelling stood quite near,
By the monastery. From here
A good mile off the rich man dwelt.
Many children life had dealt
The poor man; but his wealthy brother
Had only one child and no other,   1070
A wedded daughter. The abbot, then,
With much adroitness led the men
To reach agreement with his plan:
Since it was the poorer man
Who lived nearby, it would be well
For him to take the child to dwell
Not far off, and to rear it there.*
Whenever people asked him where
The child had come from, he should lie,
Always giving this reply: 1080
It was his niece's son, none other
Than the grandson of his brother
(A more ingenious artifice
He could not have devised than this),
And that they'd kept it here at hand*
Until they'd eaten something, and
As soon as mass was out again
They wished to ask the abbot then
To be so kind as to baptize
The child himself, and in this wise   1090
Obtain God's grace and their devotion.
It was a good and clever notion.
   The abbot took the child's supplies,
The cloth of silk, the gold likewise;
And to the poor man who would care

der sich des kindes underwant
zwô marke von golde,
dâ mitę erz ziehen solde,
dem andern eine marke,
daz erz hæle starke.   1100
daz ander truoc er von dan,
der vil sælige man.
vil wol gehielt er im daz,
dêswâr er enmöhte baz,
wandę erz ze gewinne kêrte
unz er imz wol gemêrte.
    Der arme vischære niht enliez
er entætę als in sîn herre hiez.
dô im der mitte tac kam,
daz kint er an den arm nam: 1110
sîn wîp gie im allez mite
nâch gebiurlîchem site
ze klôster, dâ er den abbet sach
under sînen bruodern. er sprach:
'herrę, iu sendet diz kint,
liute die iu willic sint,
mîns bruoder tohter und ir man,
und geloubent starke dar an,
ob irz selbe toufet,
dem kinde sî gekoufet   1120
dâ mitę ein sæligez leben,
und geruochet im iuwern namen geben.'
    Diu bete was der münche spot.
si sprâchen: 'seht (sô helfę iu got)
ze disem gebiurischen man,
wie wol er sîne rede kan.'
der herrę emphie die rede wol
als der diemüete sol.
als er daz kint rehtę ersach,
vor sîner bruoderschaft er sprach: 1130
'ez ist ein sô schœne kint:
sît si des gotes hûses sint,
dêswâr wir suln inz niht versagen.'

For the child he then and there
Gave two gold marks, thus to employ:
With these he was to rear the boy.
One mark he gave the rich man, too,
To keep concealed all that he knew.   1100
The pious abbot carried thence
The rest, and with great diligence
Invested it as best he could
To best avail for the child's good:
So well did he employ the gold,
That the sum grew severalfold.

  Now the poor fisher, in each way,
His lord, the abbot, did obey.
At noon without unseemly haste
Upon his arm the child he placed.   1110
His wife accompanied him, too,
As was the peasants' wont to do.
They sought the cloister where he found
The abbot with his brothers round.
"Lord, this child is sent to you
By people in your service who,"
The fisher said, "heed your command:
My brother's daughter, namely, and
Her husband who in faith maintain
The child the good life will obtain   1120
If you, yourself, should condescend
Both to baptize it and extend
Your name to christen it." His plea
Amused the monks. They said, "Just see,
This peasant! Gracious me! How good
He is at speeches!" As one should
Who practices humility,
The abbot listened graciously.
When to the child his gaze then sped,
Before his brotherhood he said: 1130
"Beauteous is the child we see!
Verily, we should grant their plea
Since this is their God's House* indeed."

daz kint hiez er ze toufe tragen.
er huop ez selbę und hiez es sus
nâch sînem namen, Grêgôrjus.
　Dô daz kint die toufę emphie,
der abbet sprach: 'sît ich nû hie
sîn geistlich vater worden bin,
durch mînes heiles gewin　　　　　　　　　1140
sô wil ich ez iemer hân
(ez ist sô sæliclich getân)
vil gernę an mînes kindes stat.'
vil minneclichen er dô bat
den sînen vischære
daz er sîn vlîzic wære.
er sprach: 'nû ziuch mirz schône,
daz ich dirs iemer lône.'
daz kint hulfen starke
die sîne zwô marke,　　　　　　　　　　　1150
daz man sîn deste baz phlac:
ouch lie der herrę unmanigen tac
er enwolde selbe spehen
wie daz kint wære bèsehen.

　Dô der vischærę und sîn wîp
über des süezen kindes lîp
sô rehte vlîzic wâren
unz ze sehs jâren,
der abbet nam ez dô von in
zuo im in daz klôster hin　　　　　　　　　1160
und kleidetez mit solher wât
diu phäflichen stât
und hiezz diu buoch lêren.
swaz ze triuwen und zêren
und ze vrümikeit gezôch,
wie lützel ez dâ von vlôch!
wie gernez âne slege mit bete

He bade them to the font proceed.
  Sponsoring the child then thus,*
With his own name, Gregorius.*
The priest baptized him, and said then,
"Since here, before the eyes of men,
As this child's godfather I've stood,
For the sake of my soul's good,   1140
Strong is my wish that now it be
In child's stead a son to me—
With what charm has it been blessed!"
With kindly warmth came his request
Asking his fisher that he spare
No effort in the infant's care.
He said, "The child rear well for me,
That I may always gratefully
Repay you." Now of such great force
Were the child's two marks, of course,   1150
That he was given better care.
Then, too, it was a day most rare
On which the priest failed to appear
To see how they the child did rear.

> Gregorius receives his education at the mon-
> astery school.

  Now when the fisher and his wife
Had zealously cared for the life
Of this sweet child till it attained
Six years of age,* the priest regained
The child from them, and took the lad
Home to the cloister, where he bade   1160
That he be garbed as dedicate
To the ecclesiastic state,
And bade that he be taught booklore.
How little did the child ignore
What led to honor and decency,
To excellence and loyalty!
How glad he was upon behest

sînes meisters willen tete!
ez enlie sich niht betrâgen
ez enwolde dingelîchs vrâgen   1170
diu guot ze wizzenne sint
als ein sæligez kint.
    Diu kint diu vor drin jâren
zuo gesetzet wâren,
mit kunst ez diu sô schiere ervuor
daz der meister selbe swuor,
er gesæhe von aller hande tugent
nie sô sinnerîche jugent.
er was (dâ enliuge ich iu niht an)
der jâre ein kint, der witze ein man.   1180
    An sîm einleften jâre
dô enwas zewâre
dehein bezzer grammaticus
danne daz kint Grêgôrjus.
dar nâch in den jâren drin
dô gebezzerte sich sîn sin
alsô daz im dîvînitas
garwe durchliuhtet was:
diu kunst ist von der goteheit.
swaz im vür wart geleit   1190
daz lîp und sêle vrumende ist,
des ergreif er ie den houbetlist.
dar nâch las er von lêgibus
und daz kint wart alsus
in dem selben liste
ein edel lêgiste:
diu kunst sprichet von der ê.
er hete noch gelernet mê,
wan daz er wart geirret dran,
als ich iu wol gesagen kan.   1200
    Ez leit der vischære
von armuot grôze swære.
sîne huobe lâgen ûf dem sê:
des wart sîm lîbe dicke wê,
wande er sich alsus nerte,

To do his teacher's each request
Without the rod! He did not mind
Asking questions of every kind   1170
About whatever would permit
A blessed child to benefit.
   Those pupils who three years before
Had been enrolled he did outsoar
So swiftly in ability,
His very teacher openly
Confessed he'd never seen a youth
Of more intelligence (the truth
I tell you now): he was in age
A child; in mental life, a sage.   1180
   On reaching his eleventh year*
He had no one there his peer.
There was no better *grammaticus*
Than this young child, Gregorius.
The next three years that he there spent
His mind improved to such extent
That *divinitas* became
Pellucid for him—thus we name
The study of theology.
Whatever question there might be   1190
Of what does soul and body good,
He got the point and understood.
In *legibus* the child did then
Pursue his studies, and again,
Likewise in this, reached eminence
As legist of great excellence.
With law does this art have to do.
And I can tell you: this is true;
Far greater learning he'd have gained
Had he therefrom not been restrained.   1200
   Dire Poverty held her hard hand
Upon the fisher by the strand.
What fields he tilled lay in the sea,
And that caused him great misery.
For there he gained his livelihood

sîniu kint erwerte
dem bittern hunger alle tage
niuwan mit sînem bejage,
ê er daz kint vunde.
ouch wart dâ zestunde   1210
wol gesenftet sîn leben,
dô im wurden gegeben
von golde zwô marke:
dô bezzerten sich starke
alle sîne sache
an getregedę und an gemache.
nu enlie sîn ungewizzen wîp
nie geruowen sînen lîp
von tägelîcher vrâge.
si saztę im manige lâge: 1220
ir liste kêrte si dar zuo
beidiu spâte unde vruo
wie si daz vernæme
von wanne daz golt kæme.
vil manigen eit si im swuor
unz daz si an im ervuor
von wanne im daz golt was komen,
als ir ê wol habet vernomᴧn.
dô daz wîp wol bevant
daz ez nieman was erkant   1230
wer Grêgôrjus wære,
nu enbrâhte siz niht ze mære.
si truoc ez schône, daz ist wâr,
unz an sîn vünfzehende jâr.
    Nû hete diu vrouwe Sælikeit
allen wîs an in geleit
ir vil stætigez marc.
er was schœne unde starc,
er was getriuwe unde guot
und hete geduldigen muot.   1240
er hete künste gnuoge,
zuht unde vuoge.
er hetę unredelîchen zorn

And struggled on as best he could
His children's hunger to appease
And, at the ocean's mercy, ease
Their daily bitter lot with naught
Save with whatever fish he caught.   1210
So had it been until the day
He found the child; and then straightway,
As soon as there were in his hand
The two gold marks, his to command,
Fewer grew his many cares;
Better grew all his affairs:
His nourishment and ease of life.
    Now his unreasonable wife
Kept nagging him, and gave no peace,
Through daily questions without cease.   1220
She laid him many snares, directing
Her guile and cunning to detecting
Whence the gold had come. Both late
And soon she pestered her poor mate.
Not till she'd often sworn him fast
To keep all hid did she at last
(And this you have before been told)
Hear how he had obtained the gold.
Now when the woman did find out
That no one knew, without a doubt,   1230
Of Gregory's identity,
She did not blab but prudently—
And this is true—from talk refrained
Till he the age of fifteen gained.
    Now Lady Bountiful* had truly
Placed her mark on him, and duly
Stamped him with her lasting seal
In every way with utmost zeal.
He was strong and handsome, too—
Loyal, patient, good, and true.   1240
Many a skill did he possess;
Well reared was he, of good address.
Unseemly wrath he turned away

mit senftem muote verkorn.
alle tagẹ er vriunt gewan
und verlôs dar under nieman.
sîne vreude und sîn klagen
kundẹ er ze rehter mâze tragen.
lêre was er undertân
und milte des er mohte hân, 1250
genendic swâ er solde,
ein zage swâ er wolde,
den kinden ze mâze
ûf der wîsen strâze.
sîn wort gewan nie widerwanc.
er entet niht âne vürgedanc,
als im diu wîsheit gebôt:
des enwart er nie schamerôt
von deheiner sîner getât.
er suochte gnâde unde rât 1260
zallen zîten an got
und behielt starke sîn gebot.

   Got erloubetem Wunsche über in
daz er lîp unde sin
meisterte nâch sîm werde.
swâ von ouch ûf der erde
dehein man ze lobenne geschiht,
des engebrast im ouch niht.
der Wunsch hetẹ in gemeistert sô
daz er sîn was ze kinde vrô, 1270
wandẹ er nihts an im vergaz:
er hetẹ in geschaffet, kundẹ er, baz.
die liutem knappen jâhen,
alle die in gesâhen,
daz von vischære
nie geboren wære
dehein jungelinc sô sælden rîch:
ez wære harte schedelîch
daz man in niht mähte
geprîsen von geslähte, 1280
und jâhen des ze stæte,

With gentleness. New friends each day
He made, and never lost the old.
His joy and sorrow he controlled,
Not showing them excessively.
To correction he'd agree.
Of what he had he freely gave.
If need be, boldly he'd behave,   1250
But timidly if so he chose,
As befits the child who goes
On wisdom's road. He never broke
His word. In all he did and spoke
He always showed forethought, and had—
Since he did all that wisdom bade—
No cause to blush for word or deed.
God he would seek; God he would heed;
To Him he turned for counsel, and
His grace he sought, while His command   1260
He firmly kept in every way.
    God let Perfection* hold its sway
Over him, that it might mold
His mind and body and behold
A living likeness of its worth.
Whatever finds acclaim on earth
And merits praise, he did possess.
Perfection modeled his address
And person with such excellence
That it was glad in every sense   1270
To own him as its child; and so
He lacked naught that it could bestow.
He was as perfect as could be;
Perfection could no more decree.
All who saw the lad confessed
That never had so richly blessed
A youth called fishermen his kin.
A pity that his origin*
Precluded praise of pedigree!
And this they said repeatedly: 1280
If he were but of noble birth,

ob erz an gebürte hæte,
sô wære wol ein rîche lant
ze sîner vrümikeit bewant.

   Nu geviel ez eines tages sus
daz der knappe Grêgôrjus
mit sînen spilgenôzen kam
dâ si spilnes gezam.
nu gevuocte ein wunderlich geschiht
(ez enkam von sînem willen niht):   1290
er tet (daz geschach im nie mê)
des vischæres kinde alsô wê
daz ez weinen began.
sus lief ez schrîende dan.
als daz diu muoter vernam
daz ez sus weinende kam,
ir kinde si engegen lief.
in grôzen unsiten si rief:
'sich, wie weinestû sus?'
'dâ sluoc mich Grêgôrjus.'   1300
'war umbe hât er dich geslagen?'
'muoter, ich kan dirs niht gesagen.'
'sich her, tæte dû im iht?'
'muoter, weizgot nein ich niht.'
'wâ ist er nû?' 'bî jenem sê.'
'wê mir armer, wê!
er tumber gouch vil betrogen!
hân ich daz an im erzogen
daz er mir bliuwet mîniu kint,
sô wol gevriunt sô si hie sint?   1310
dînen vriunden zimet daz niht wol
daz ich diz laster dulden sol
von einem sô gewanten man
der nie mâge hie gewan.

A mighty realm upon this earth
Could be entrusted to his hand
And flourish under his command.

> Gregorius learns from his foster mother that he
> is a foundling, and he tells the abbot of his wish
> to leave.

Now one fine day it happened thus:
The young lad, Gregorius,
With his playmates had gone out
To where they liked to play about.
Now there occurred a strange event
(It happened quite without intent):   1290
So hard a sudden blow he dealt
The fisher's son, who'd never felt
The like before, that he began
To weep aloud, and straightway ran
Away from there with great outcry.
Hearing him as he drew nigh,
Excitedly his mother ran
To him, and shouting she began:
"Here, tell me, child, what makes you cry?"
"Gregorius struck me; that is why!"   1300
"Now tell me why he hit you so."
"Mother, I really do not know."
"Look, did you hurt him anywhere?"
"God knows, I didn't, not hide nor hair!"
"Now then, tell me, where is he?"
"There, near the beach." "Oh, my, poor me!
The stupid fool! Conceited ass!
Did I rear him for this, alas!
To have him beat my children dear,
Who are so well connected here?   1310
Your relatives won't find it fit
To have me stomach and permit
Such an outrage from anyone
Who has no kindred here—no, none!

daz dich tar gebliuwen der
der sich hât verrunnen her,
daz ist mir iemer ein leit.
wan daz man imz durch got vertreit,
man duldetz unlange vrist.
jâ enweiz nieman wer er ist.   1320
[und ist daz ich nû leben sol,
ich sagez al der werlde wol
daz er ein vuntkint ist
(sô helfe mir der heilige Krist),
swie hôhẹ er nu sî gesezzen.
des hât er gar vergezzen
daz er sô jæmerlich wart vunden
in ein vaz gebunden
in einer barke ûf dem sê.
sol er mînem kinde tuon wê,   1330
man duldetz unlange vrist.
ja enweiz hie nieman wer er ist.]
wê mir, wes ist im gedâht?
der tiuvel hât in her brâht
mir zeiner harnschar.
ja erkennẹ ich sîn geverte gar,
er vundene dürftige.
wan wolde er daz man verswige
sîn schentlîche sache?
sô lebetẹ er mit gemache.   1340
die vische sîn verwâzen,
daz si in niene vrâzen,
do er ûf den sê geworfen wart.
er ergreif ein sælige vart,
daz er dem apte zuo kam.
wan daz er in dînem vater nam
und sîn almuosenære ist,
sô müesẹ er uns, wizze Krist,
anders undertænic sîn:
er müesẹ uns rinder unde swîn   1350
trîben ûz unde in.
war tet dîn vater sînen sin,

That he has dared to thrash you, he,
A stray waif—that will always be
A grief to me. Unless, indeed,
For God's sake one paid it no heed,
In no time he would have to go;
For where he comes from, none here know.   1320
If I'm to keep on living now,
I'll tell the world, I do avow,
That he is but a foundling child*
(So help me Christ, holy and mild);
Though high his present station be
He has forgotten totally
That he so pitifully was found
Within a little chest, fast bound,
In a bark upon the brine.
If he's to harm a child of mine,   1330
In no time he would have to go;
For where he comes from, none here know.
        "Woe's me! What can he have in mind?
The Devil must have felt inclined
To send him here as a great bane
To my existence, and quite plain
Is all his history to me.
That beggar lad! That foundling, he!
Why didn't he want such shame concealed
And not have his disgrace revealed?   1340
He'd live in comfort and in ease!
May a curse all those fish seize
That failed to swallow him when he,
The wretch, was cast into the sea.
Lucky for him his voyage here
Brought him into the abbot's sphere!*
Had the priest the lad not seized
From your father, and then pleased
To keep him as his almoner,
God knows, quite differently he'd stir   1350
For us: he'd take care of the swine
And to and fro he'd herd the kine.

do er in mit vrostiger hant
ûf dem gemeinen sê vant,
daz er in dem apte liez
und in im selben niene hiez
dienen sam durch allez reht
tæte sîn schalc und sîn kneht ?'
  Grêgôrjus, dô er daz kint gesluoc,
dar umbe was er trûric gnuoc   1360
und lief im ze hûse nâch.
dar umbe was im alsô gâch
daz er des sêre vorhte
daz im daz kint entworhte
sîner ammen minne.
nu erhôrtẹ er si dar inne
schelten âne mâze.
nu gestuont er an der strâze
unz er den itewîz vernam
und unverwister dinge kam   1370
gar an ein ende,
daz er ellende
wære in dem lande,
wan si in ofte nande.
sîn vreude wart verborgen
in disen niuwen sorgen.
er gedâhtẹ im grôzer swære,
ob disiu rede wære
ein lüge oder ein wârheit,
die sîn amme hete geseit,   1380
unde gâhte dô zehant
ze klôster, dâ er den abbet vant,
und nam den getriuwen man
von den liuten sunder dan.
  Er sprach: 'vil lieber herre,
ich kan iu niht sô verre
gedanken mit dem munde,
als, ob ich kunde,
vil gerne tæte.
nu belîbẹ ich dar an stæte   1390

When on the high seas, with chilled hand,*
Your father found him far from land,
Where was his head, to hand him so
To the priest, and to forgo
His due by law, and his rights waive
Of keeping him as serf or slave?"
   Gregorius was very sad
At having struck the fisher's lad,   1360
And after him he quickly hurried.
So great his haste, because he worried
His foster mother, through this lad,
For him would lose what love she had.
He heard her loudly shout inside
Abuse in a relentless tide.
From off the street he did not stir
Till he at length had heard from her
Her last vituperative remark;
And what had hitherto been dark   1370
Was at an end, and clear became
(Since oft she spoke of him by name):
That he was an outcast banned,*
An alien stranger in this land.
All his happiness and joy
These new misgivings did destroy.
In deep distress at what he'd heard,
He pondered over every word
His foster mother had just said—
Was it false, or true instead?   1380
To seek the priest without delay,
To the cloister he made his way,
And, finding the good abbot then,
Took him aside, apart from men.
   "O, my beloved lord," he spoke,
"Never can I words evoke
Of fitting gratitude to you,
And give you thanks as I would do
If eloquent I were of tongue.
Him, to Whom I've always clung,   1390

daz ich unz an mîns endes zil
den dar umbe biten wil
der deheiner guottât
niemer ungelônet lât
daz er iu des lône
mit der himelischen krône
(dêswâr des hân ich michel reht)
daz ir mich ellenden kneht
von einem vunden kinde
vür allez iuwer gesinde   1400
sô zartlichen habet erzogen.
leider ich bin des betrogen,
ich enbin niht der ich wânde sîn.
nû sult ir, lieber herre mîn,
mir durch got gebieten.
ich sol und muoz mich nieten
nôt und angest (daz ist reht)
als ein ellender kneht.
mir hât mîn amme des verjehen
(in einem zornę ist daz geschehen)   1410
daz ich vunden bin.
beidiu lîp unde sin
benimet mir diu unêre,
vernim ichs iemer mêre.
ich enhœre si weizgot niemer mê,
wandę ich niht langer hie bestê.
jâ vindę ich eteswâ daz lant
daz dâ niemen ist erkant
wie ich her komen bin.
ich hân die kunst und ouch den sin,   1420
ich genise wol, und wil ez got.
sô sêre vürhte ich den spot:
ich woldę ê sîn dâ nieman ist,
ê daz ich über dise vrist
belibe hie ze lande.
ja vertrîbet mich diu schande.
diu wîp sint sô unverdaget:
sît siz eines hât gesaget,

I shall continue steadfastly—
Until the day Death seizes me—
To beseech, and pray the Lord,
Who lets no good deed lack reward,
That He accord to you your due,
And Heaven's crown bestow on you
(I have great cause to beg Him so) ;
Such great kindness did you show
That me, a wretched outcast slave,
From foundling's state, you rearing gave   1400
Above your servants, great and small—
You set me higher than them all.
Unluckily I was deceived—
I'm someone other than I believed.
    "O, my dear master, for God's sake,
Bid me now departure take.
Now I should, and now I must,
As homeless servant (that is just),
Espouse and suffer tribulation.
My foster mother, in vexation,   1410
While greatly angered, did avow
I was a foundling. If I now
Were often taunted with my shame,
My life and reason that would claim.
I'll hear no more of this disgrace ;
God knows, I mean to leave this place.
Somewhere, perhaps, I may suppose,
There is a land where no one knows
How I first came here to you.
I'm skilful and can reason, too.   1420
If God so will, I'll stay alive ;
But mockery I'd not survive.
I dread it so, I'd rather far
Be where no human beings are
Than in this country longer stay.
Truly shame drives me away.
All women tattle so and prate.
Since once my tale she did relate,

sô wizzenz vil schiere
drîe unde viere   1430
und dar nâch alle die hie sint.'

    Der abbet sprach: 'vil liebez kint,
nû losẹ: ich wil dir râten wol
als ich mînem lieben sol
den ich von kinde gezogen hân.
got hât vil wol ze dir getân:
er hât von sînen minnen
an lîbe und an sinnen
dir vil vrîe wal gegeben,
daz dû nû selbe dîn leben   1440
maht schephen unde kêren
ze schanden oder zêren.
nû muostû disen selben strît
in disen jâren, ze dirre zît
under disen beiden
nâch dîner kür scheiden,
swaz dû dir wilt erwerben,
genesen oder verderben,
daz dû des nû beginnen solt.
sun, nû wis dir selben holt   1450
und volge mîner lêre
(sô hâstû tugent und êre
vür laster und vür spot erkorn),
daz dir durch dînen tumben zorn
der werkẹ iht werde sô gâch
daz dich geriuwe dar nâch.
dû bist ein sælic jungelinc:
ze wunsche stânt dir dîniu dinc,
dîn begin ist harte guot,
die liute tragent dir holden muot   1460
die in disen landen sint.

No time will pass before first three,
Then four hear it, and presently   1430
Everyone will know it here."

> Gregorius is unable to accept the abbot's counsel
> to remain. He expresses his great longing to
> become a knight and is knighted by the abbot.

The abbot said, "My child, most dear,
Hearken! I would counsel you,
As I'm in duty bound to do
For one who is to me endeared
And whom from childhood I have reared.
Most gracious has God been to you,*
And through His love did you endue
With freedom of the will, assigned
To both your body and your mind,   1440
That you, yourself, in this respect
Can mold your life, and thus direct
Its course to honor or to shame.
Since your departure you proclaim,
At once, now, at your tender age,
In this conflict you must engage,
And make your choice between the two,
Deciding which you wish to do:
Attain salvation, or be undone.*
    "To your own self be true, my son,   1450
And follow all my teaching (hence,
You will choose moral excellence
And honor rather than disgrace
And ignominy), and not race
Apace on foolish anger's path
To rash and hasty deeds of wrath
That you will later rue! A youth
You are who's well endowed. In truth,
With you things could not better stand.
You've started well. All in this land   1460
Are favorably disposed toward you.

nû volge mir, mîn liebez kint.
dû bist der phafheit gewon:
nû enziuch dich niht dâ von.
dû wirst der buoche wîse:
sô bin ich jâre grîse,
mîn lîp ist schiere gelegen.
nû wil ich dir vür wâr verphlegen
daz ich dir nû erwirbe,
swenne ich dar nâch erstirbe,   1470
umbe unser samenunge,
alte und junge,
daz si dich nement ze herren.
nû waz mac dir gewerren
einer tœrinne klaffen?
ouch trûwe ich wol geschaffen
daz diu rede vür dise stunt
niemer kumet vür ir munt.'
   Grêgôrjus sprach: 'herre,
ir habet got vil verre   1480
an mir armen gêret
und iuwer heil gemêret
und nû daz beste vür geleit.
nû ist mir mîn tumpheit
alsô sêre erbolgen,
si enlât mich iu niht volgen.
mich vertrîbent drîe sache
ze mînem ungemache
ûzer disem lande.
daz ein ist diu schande   1490
die ich von itewîze hân.
sô ist diu ander sô getân
diu mich ouch verjaget hin:
ich weiz nû daz ich niene bin
disse vischæres kint.
nû waz ob mîne vordern sint
von solhem geslähte
daz ich wol werden mähte
ritter, ob ich hæte

"Now then, my dear child, heed my view.
You're used to priests and priests' ways:
Do not turn aside your gaze,
But stay with us. You'll grow to be
A learned cleric. Life for me
Is almost over, for I'm gray
And old in years. I wish to say,
And not keep hid, that I'll engage
To win both old and young in age   1470
Within these walls to name you head
Here in the cloister, once I'm dead.
I do assure you now of that.
How can a foolish woman's chat
Or idle babble injure you?
Besides, I feel most certain, too,
I'll readily on her prevail
Never again to tell this tale."

"Sir, through all you've done for me,"
Gregorius said, "wretch though I be,   1480
Great honor and respect you've shown
To God, and in His eyes you've grown
In merit. You've offered and defined
What's best. Yet my young, foolish mind,
So grievously provoked, prevents
My heeding your wise arguments.
Three things drive me away from here,
To my sorrow. First: I fear
The shame, to which I now am heir,
And insult that I can not bear.   1490
The nature of the second thing
Is such that, likewise, through its sting
I'm driven from this land to go:
I'm not the fisher's child, I know.
What if of such high degree
Should prove to be my ancestry
That readily I now well could
Become a knight, if so I would,
And if I were equipped aright?

den willen undz geræte ?   1500
weizgot nû was ie mîn muot,
hæte ich geburt und daz guot,
ich würde gerne ritter.
daz süeze honec ist bitter
einem ieglîchen man
der ez niezen niene kan.
ir habet daz süeziste leben
daz got der werlde hât gegeben:
swer imz ze rehte hât erkorn,
der ist sælic geborn.   1510
ich belibe hie lîhte stæte,
ob ich den willen hæte
des ich leider niht enhân.
ze ritterschefte stât mîn wân.'
     'Sun, dîn rede enist niht guot:
durch got bekêre dînen muot.
swer sich von phaffen bilde
gote machet wilde
unde ritterschaft begât,
der muoz mit maniger missetât   1520
verwürken sêle unde lîp.
swelh man oder wîp
sich von gote wendet,
der wirt dâ von geschendet
und der helle verselt.
sun, ich hete dich erwelt
zeinem gotes kinde:
ob ichz an dir vinde,
des wil ich iemer wesen vrô.'
     Grêgôrjus antwurte im dô: 1530
'ritterschaft daz ist ein leben,
der im die mâze kan gegeben,
sô enmac nieman baz genesen.
er mac gotes ritter gerner wesen
danne ein betrogen klôsterman.'
'sun, nû vürhte ich dîn dar an:
du enkanst ze ritterschefte niht.

I've always wished to be a knight;   1500
God knows, I've always thought of it,
Had I but rank that would permit
My being one, and means to live.
  "The sweetest honey that you give
To one who dislikes honey's savor
Will for him have bitter flavor.
The sweetest life of all you live*
That God the world of men did give.
Born blessed the man who chose this life
Meetly, without inner strife.   1510
Here I'd remain, it well could be,
If such were my proclivity.
Alas, I do not so aspire,
For knighthood is all my desire."
  "My son, you speak not wisdom's part.
For God's sake, change your mind and heart.
The religious who will turn
In estrangement, God to spurn,
And the life of knighthood lead,
Is apt through many a wicked deed   1520
His body and his soul to lose.
Anyone who would so choose,
Man or woman, to turn away
From God, becomes dishonor's prey
And is surrendered thus to Hell.
You I'd chosen here to dwell,
An oblate to the Lord, and I
My happiness would not deny
Could I attain that end in you."
  Gregorius replied to him anew: 1530
"The life of knighthood is the best
Of lives and makes a person blessed,
Provided he gives it its due.
As God's knight he'd be happier, too,
Than if a false monk's life* he led."
  "My dearest son, what you have said
Stirs my concern for you: you show

sô man dich danne gesiht
unbehendeclichen rîten,
sô muostû zallen zîten   1540
dulden ander ritter spot.
noch erwint, vil lieber sun, durch got.'
'herre, ich bin ein junger man
und lerne des ich niht enkan.
swar ich die sinne wenden wil,
des gelerne ich schiere vil.'
'sun, mir saget vil maniges munt
dem ze ritterschaft ist kunt:
swer ze schuole belîbe
unz er dâ vertrîbe   1550
ungeriten zwelf jâr,
der müeze iemer vür wâr
gebâren nâch den phaffen.
dû bist vil wol geschaffen
zeinem gotes kinde
und ze kôrgesinde:
diu kutte gestuont nie manne baz.'
    'Herre, nû versuochet ouch daz
und gebet mir ritterlîche wât:
dêswâr ob si mir missestât,   1560
sô gan ich ir wol eim andern man
und lege die kutten wider an.
herre, iu ist vil wâr geseit:
ez bedarf vil wol gewizzenheit,
swer guot ritter wesen sol.
ouch hân ichz gelernet wol
von kinde in mînem muote hie:
ez enkam ûz mînem sinne nie.
ich sage iu, sît der stunde
daz ich bedenken kunde   1570
beidiu übel unde guot,
sô stuont ze ritterschaft mîn muot.
ich enwart nie mit gedanke
ein Beier noch ein Vranke:
swelh ritter zHenegou,

That of knighthood you nothing know.
If you're seen riding clumsily,
You'll have to bear the mockery 1540
Of other knights. Give up the thought,
As, for God's sake, my son, you ought."
  "Sir, I am young and shall still grow;
There's time to learn what I don't know.
No matter to what my mind I turn,
In short time I shall that learn."
  "My son, full many who know well*
Of knights and knighthood I've heard tell:
Whoever for twelve years remains
At school, and never holds the reins 1550
To practice horsemanship, in truth
Will show the training of his youth
And always act the priest. But you
Nature did so well endue
As monk or chorister: no one
Has ever worn the cowl, my son,
With more becomingness than you."
  "Sir, put this to the proof, then, too:
A knight's apparel give to me;
If ill it suits me, cheerfully 1560
I'll give it up to other men
And surely don the cowl again.
Much you have heard, sir, is quite right.
Whoever would be a good knight,
Great knowledge must that man possess.
But I have learned it nonetheless,
And myself in spirit taught
From earliest childhood; for the thought
Has never left me since I could
First discern evil from good.* 1570
Thus steadfastly with all my might
I've always longed to be a knight.
No Bavarian* in my mind's eye,
Nor Franconian knight was I.
But always the knight with best manège

zBrâbant und zHaspengou
zorsę ie aller beste gesaz,
sô kan ichz mit gedanken baz.
herre, swaz ich der buoche kan,
dâ engerou mich nie niht an   1580
und kundę ir gerne mêre:
iedoch sô man mich sêre
ie unz her zen buochen twanc,
sô turnierte mîn gedanc.
sô man mich buoche wente,
wie sich mîn herze sente
und mîn gedanc spilte
gegen einem schilte!
ouch was mir ie vil ger
vür den griffel zuo dem sper,   1590
vür die veder zem swerte:
daz ist des ich ie gerte.
mînen gedanken wart nie baz
dan sô ich zorse gesaz
und den schilt ze halse genam
und daz sper als ez gezam
und daz undern arm gesluoc
und mich daz ors von sprunge truoc.
sô liez ich schenkel vliegen:
die kundę ich sô gebiegen   1600
daz ich daz ors mit sporen sluoc
weder zen lanken noch in den buoc,
dâ hinder eines vingers breit
dâ der surzengel ist geleit.
neben der mane vlugen diu bein:
ob des sateles ich schein
als ich wære gemâlet dar,
ders möhte hân genomen war.
mit guoter gehabe ich reit
ânes lîbes arbeit: 1610
ich gap im senften gelimph
als ez wære mîn schimph,
und sô ich mich mit sporen vleiz

In Brabant, Hainaut, or in Liège,
Astride a horse—far better than he
I'd always think that I could be.
Sir, the booklore I have gained
I have never yet disdained   1580
And gladly would I gather more.
No matter how—now and before—
To books I was kept and confined,
I always jousted in my mind;
And all the while to books I waxed
Accustomed, how my heart was taxed
With yearning for a shield, and how
My mind sported with armor! Now,
I've always longed more for the spear
Than for the style; a sword's more dear   1590
To me than any pen could be.
A sword I've wished for constantly.
    "My happiest thought was when I strode
A horse, and on his back so rode:
At my throat my shield I'd clasp*
Before me; then my lance I'd grasp
And put beneath my arm in place;
In headlong gallop off I'd race
Upon my steed. And I would prove
Bewinged, for so my thighs I'd move   1600
That the spurs I'd give my horse
Not in the flanks or groin, of course,
Nor in the shoulders, but toward the rear
Behind the girth strap, just a mere
Finger's breadth away. I'd speed
With legs close to the mane. Indeed,
In the saddle I would hold
My seat so perfectly controlled,
I'd look as were I painted on;
Relaxed I'd ride, all effort gone;   1610
My posture would such ease betray
As were I sporting in mere play.
When with diligence I'd drill,

ûf einen langen puneiz,
sô kundẹ ich wol gewenden
daz ors ze beiden henden.
gejustiertẹ ich ie wider keinen man,
dâ gevâltẹ ich nie an,
mîn merken würde wol bewant
zen vier nageln gegen der hant.   1620
nû helfet, lieber herre, mir
daz diu ritterlîche gir
mit werken müeze volgân:
sô habet ir wol ze mir getân.'
    'Sun, dû hâst mir vil geseit,
manic tiusch wort vür geleit,
daz mich vil sêre umbe dich
wundern muoz, crêde mich,
und weiz niht war zuo daz sol:
ich vernæme kriechisch als wol.   1630
unser meister, der dîn phlac
mit lêre unz an disen tac,
von dem hâstû si niht vernomen.
von swannen si dir zuo sî komen,
dû bist, daz merkẹ ich wol dar an,
des muotes niht ein klôsterman.
nû wil ich dichs niht wenden mê.
got gebe daz dir wol ergê
und gebe dir durch sîne kraft
heil ze dîner ritterschaft.'   1640
    Nû schuof er daz man im sneit
von dem selben phelle kleit
den er dâ bî im vant:
ez enkam nie bezzer in daz lant.
er sach wol daz im was gâch
unde machetẹ in dar nach
ritter als im wol tohte
sô er schierist mohte.

Using my spurs, to gain in skill
At long-charge tilting, to each side
I'd veer my steed at will and ride
Now to the left, now to the right.
When I'd joust against a knight,
Through careful aim his shield I'd hit
Where the four studs lie opposite   1620
His hand—and never fail. Sweet lord,
Fulfilment of my wish accord
For knighthood in reality;
You'll show great kindness thus to me."
    "You've told me much, son. I'm confused*
By many German words you've used.
These words I am amazed to hear,
Crede me,* from you; not clear
Is what they mean, and as you speak
I might as well be hearing Greek.   1630
It's most unlikely that you've heard
From our instructor, any such word
In all your schooling to this day.
No matter where you learned to say
These words, to me they this impart:
You are no monk in mind or heart.
Your going I'll no more delay.
God prosper you upon your way,
And may He through His graciousness
Grant you in knighthood great success."   1640
    The abbot then had raiment made
From the silks and rich brocade
Found with the child; one could command
No finer fabrics in the land.
The priest, perceiving the lad's state—
So eager that he scarce could wait—
With all haste had him made knight,*
As was his privilege and his right.

Grêgôrjus, dô er ritter wart,
dannoch hetẹ er im niht enbart   1650
umbe sîn tavel und umbe sîn golt.
er was im alsô starke holt
daz erz in hal durch einen list.
er gedâhte: 'sît er nû ritter ist
und er des guotes niene hât,
sô hœret er lîhte mînen rât
und belîbet noch durch guot gemach.'
er versuochtez aber unde sprach:
'noch belîp, lieber sun, bî mir.
dêswâr ich gevüege dir   1660
ein alsô rîche hîrât
diu wol nâch dînem willen stât
unde gibe dir al die vrist
daz dû vil schône varende bist.
dû hâst gewunnen ritters namen:
nû muostu dich dîner armuot schamen.
nû waz touc dîn ritterschaft,
du enhetest guotes die kraft?
nu enkumestû in dehein lant
dâ dû iemen sîst erkant: 1670
da enhâstû vriunt noch vorder habe.
sich, dâ verdirbestû abe.
noch bekêre dînen muot
und belîp: daz ist dir guot.'
    Grêgôrjus sprach: 'herre,
versuochetz niht sô verre.
woldẹ ich gemach vür êre,
sô volgetẹ ich iuwer lêre
und lieze nider mînen muot:
wan mîn gemach wære hie guot.   1680
jâ tuot ez manigem schaden
der der habẹ ist überladen:
der verlît sich durch gemach,

Gregorius expresses his determination to pursue knighthood at all costs.

Though Gregory now knight's rank had,
The priest had not informed the lad   1650
About his tablet and his gold.
His great love caused him to withhold
This knowledge for a subtle aim.
"Since now to knight's name he has claim,"
He thought, "but lacks all property,
He'll heed my counsel readily
And surely he will here remain,
A comfortable life to gain."
Once more the abbot tried, and said,
"Stay yet by me, dear son. You'll wed   1660
As wealthily as you desire;
I'll see to that. What you require
I'll give you, so that you, indeed,
A very pleasant life will lead.
Though knight in name you now may be,
You'll feel the shame of poverty.
What use is knighthood then to you
If with no means you must make do?
No matter to what land you go,
You're known to none; none you will know.   1670
You'll have no wealth or consequence
Nor friends. Now think, if you go hence
You'll perish. Change your mind, and stay;
It's for your good in every way."
    "My lord, insist not so," demurred
The knight. "If comfort I preferred
To honor,* my intention now
I would give up, and I would bow
To your instructions, for it's clear
I'd be most comfortable here.   1680
Yet many men are greatly harmed
If they possess too much, and, charmed
By ease, wax indolent. This never

daz dem armen nie geschach
der dâ rehte ist gemuot:
wan der urbort umbe guot
den lîp manigen enden.
wie möhtę erz baz gewenden?
wan ob er sich gewirden kan,
er wirt vil lîhtę ein sælic man   1690
und über älliu diu lant
vür manigen herren erkant.
daz ich heizę ein arm man,
dâ bin ich unschuldic an.
ich trage sį alle samet hie,
die huobe die mir mîn vater lie.
sîtz mir nû sô geziuhet
daz mich diu Sælde vliuhet
und ich niuwan ir gruoz
mit vrümikeit gedienen muoz,   1700
dêswâr ich kan si wol erjagen,
si enwelle sich mir mê versagen
dan si sich noch versagete
der si ze rehte jagete.
sus sol man si erloufen,
mit kumber sælde koufen.
dâ enzwîvel ich niht an,
wirdę ich ein rehte vrumer man
an lîbe und an sinne,
ich engediene wol ir minne: 1710
unde bin ich aber ein zage,
so enmüezę ich niemer drîe tage
geleben, so ich hinnen kêre.
waz soldę ich âne êre?
ob ich mit rehter arbeit,
mit sinne und mit manheit
erwirbe guot und êre,
des prîset man mich mêre
dan dem sîn vater wunder lie
und daz mit schanden zegie.   1720
wes bedarf ich mê dannę ich hân?

Befalls the poor man who will ever
Maintain the proper point of view;
For he'll exert himself anew
In many ways wealth to obtain.
What's better than that? For if he gain
Respect and glory, readily
He'll grow happy, and he'll be   1690
Far more famous throughout this earth
Than many a lord of noble birth.
Surely I can not be blamed
That I a poor man must be named.
My father's acres to which I'm heir
All lightly on my back I bear.

   "Since it's my fate that I must see
Lady Bountiful* flee from me,
And that to gain her mere salute
I must be brave and resolute,   1700
I'll win her yet successfully,
If she's no more averse to me
Than to any who did essay
To win her in the proper way.
One should give this Lady chase
And, struggling hard, obtain her grace.
This I do not doubt: if I
Through my valor qualify
Both in body and in mind,
I'll earn her love, and she'll be kind.   1710
If I prove coward and faint-hearted,
Turning back when I've departed,
Not three days let me survive.
If honor's gone why stay alive?
If through skill and manly deed,
If through true effort I succeed
And have great wealth and honor won,
I'll be more famed than anyone
Who loses ignominiously
His father's splendid legacy.   1720
Do I not have what meets my needs?

mîn ors sint guot und wol getân,
mîn knehte biderbę unde guot
und hânt getriuwelîchen muot:
sô bin ich zharnasche wol.
swâ man guot bejagen sol,
da getrûwę ich harte wol genesen.
diz sol der redę ein ende wesen:
herrę, iuwern gnâden sî genigen
und des mit hulden verzigen   1730
daz ich iht langer hie bestê.'

'Sun, sô enwil ich dich niht mê
sûmen vür dise vrist
(ich sihe wol daz dir ernest ist),
swie ungernę ich dîn enbir.
lieber sun, nû ganc mit mir:
wan ich wil dich sehen lân
waz ich noch dînes dinges hân.'
  Sus vuortę in der getriuwe man
vil sêre weinende dan   1740
ûf eine kemenâten
die er vil wol berâten
mit sîdîner wæte vant
und gap im in sîne hant
sîne tavel, daz er las
wie allem sînem dinge was.
des wart er trûric unde vrô.
sîn trûren schuof sich alsô
als ich iu hie künde:
er weinde von der sünde,   1750
dâ er inne was geborn.
dâ wider hâtę er im erkorn
guote vreude dar abe,
von hôher geburt, von rîcher habe,

Both sound and handsome are my steeds;
Fit and able is each squire;
None more loyal could one desire.
Besides, fine armor do I bear.
Where one can make one's fortune, there,
I'm confident, I will succeed.
For further words there is no need.
In gratitude, sir, let me bow,
For all your kindness, and allow   1730
That I depart from here straightway."

> Gregorius learns of his tablet and wealth. With
> conflicting emotions he takes leave of the abbot
> and sets sail for parts unknown.

"My son, no more shall I delay
Your going, although sad I'll be
Without you, since I clearly see
You are resolved to go away.
Then come with me, for now, this day,
My son, I wish to show to you
What else I've kept that is your due."
Then as he shed full many a tear,
The old man, loyal and sincere,   1740
To a chamber led the way,
Where there lay stored a great array
Of silks, and here placed in his hand
The tablet that the youth now scanned
And from it learned how matters stood—
The whole account—the bad, the good.
Sorrowful he grew, yet glad.
This was the cause his sorrow had,
As I shall now to you relate.
He bewept the sinful state   1750
In which he had been born; yet, too,
He gleaned true joy, because he knew
That he was of high pedigree
And wealth possessed to such degree—

der er ê niht enweste.
dô sprach der triuwen veste
der sîn herre was gewesen:
'sun, nû hâstû wol gelesen
daz ich dich unz her hân verdaget:
dîn tavel hât dirz wol gesaget.   1760
nû hân ich mit dem golde
gebâret als ich solde
nâch dîner muoter gebote:
ich hân dirz in gote
gemêret harte starke.
vünfzic und hundert marke,
die hân wir dir gewunnen,
swie übele wirz kunnen,
von sibenzehen sît den stunden
daz wir dich êrste vunden.   1770
ich gap in drî und niht mê
die dich mir brâhten abe dem sê.
alsus vil ist dîner habe:
dâ begâstu dich schône abe
zanderm gewinne,
hâstû deheine sinne.'
     Des antwurte im Grêgôrjus
vil sêre weinende sus:
'ouwê, lieber herre,
ich bin vervallen verre   1780
âne alle mîne schulde.
wie sol ich gotes hulde
gewinnen nâch der missetât
diu hie vor mir geschriben stât?'
'vil lieber sun, daz sage ich dir.
dêswâr, daz geloube mir,
gestâstû bî der ritterschaft,
sich, sô mêret sich diu kraft
dîner tägelîchen missetât
und enwirt dîn niemer rât: 1790
dâ von sô lâ dîn irrikeit
die dû an hâst geleit

Of which he had not known before.
    The loyal priest then spoke once more,
He who had been his lord, and said,
"My son, this tablet that you've read
Has, indeed, to you revealed
What I've from you till now concealed.   1760
As to your gold, I well did try
To care for it, and to comply
With the request your mother made,
As was my duty. With God's aid
I have increased your legacy.
One hundred fifty marks, which we
Have managed to obtain for you—
Though it was hard for us to do—
Is now the sum accrued from ten
And seven gold marks you had then   1770
When you were found.* I gave but three
To them that brought you from the sea
To me—no more. Now this amount
Is yours, and—taking no account
Of gain through your own enterprise—
You can live well, if you are wise."
    Then in reply Gregorius,
Weeping bitter tears, spoke thus:
"Alas, dear master, I've sunk low
Through no guilt of my own.* Ah, woe!   1780
Dear master, how can I now win
God's grace in view of this great sin
Inscribed upon the tablet here
Before me?" "That I shall make clear
To you, beloved son. Truly—
Trust me in this—should you unduly
Persist in following knighthood's course,
The sum of all your sins, perforce,
Will grow greater, day by day;*
And you will never find a way   1790
To help yourself. Because of this,
Leave off your erring aim; dismiss

unde diene gote hie.
ja enübersach er dienest nie.
sun, nû stant im hie ze klage
und verkoufe dîne kurze tage
umbe daz êwige leben.
sun, den rât wil ich dir geben.'
'ouwê, lieber herre,
jâ ist mîn gir noch merre   1800
zuo der werlde dan ê.
ich engeruowe niemer mê
und wil iemer varnde sîn,
mir entuo noch gotes gnâde schîn
von wannẹ ich sî oder wer.'
'sun, des bewîse dich der
der dich nâch im gebildet hât,
sît dû verwirfest mînen rât.'
    Ein schef wart im gereite,
dâ man im an leite   1810
zem lîbe volleclîchen rât,
spîse, sîn golt, sîne wât.
und dô er ze scheffe ǧie,
der abbet begap in nie
unz er an daz schef getrat.
alsus rûmtẹ er daz stat.
swie sêre sî gescheiden diu tugent
under alter und under jugent,
so ergie doch von in beiden
ein jæmerlîchez scheiden.   1820
si enmohten der ougen
ein ander niht verlougen
unz si sich vor dem breiten sê
enmohten undersehen mê.

Your wrong intent, and serve God here;
For never—truly this is clear—
Has He ignored a duty done.
Submit here* to His judgment, son:
Surrender the short days you live
For life eternal. To you I give
This counsel, son." "Alas, oh woe!
Dear master, my desire does grow   1800
Intense for this world, yea, far more
Than it has ever been before.
I'll not desist from errant quest
Till God's grace makes it manifest
Who I am and whence I came."
"My son, may God Who chose your frame
In His own image grant you learn
All that, since my advice you spurn."
  A ship for him they ready made,
And everything was then purveyed   1810
Aboard in ample plenitude:
Equipment, fabrics, gold, and food.
When to the ship he made his way
Never did the abbot stray
From him till he embarked. And thus
From shore set sail Gregorius.
However youth and age may be
Unlike in sensibility,
The two felt sorrowful at heart
When time came for them both to part.   1820
They could not turn their eyes, but still
Kept looking at each other till
The widening sea between them made
Each from the other's vision fade.

Nû bôt der ellende
herze unde hende
ze himelę und bat vil verre
daz in unser herre
sandę in etelîchez lant
dâ sîn vart wære bewant.　　　　　1830
er gebôt den marnæren
daz si den winden wæren
nâch ir willen undertân
und daz schef liezen gân
swarz die winde lêrten
und anders niene kêrten.
ein starker wint dô wæte:
der beleip in stæte
und wurden in vil kurzen tagen
von einem sturmweter geslagen　　　1840
ûf sîner muoter lant.
daz was verhert und verbrant,
als ich iu ê gesaget hân,
daz ir niht mêre was verlân
niuwan ir houbetstat
diu ouch mit kumber was besat.
und als er die stat ersach,
zen marnæren er dô sprach

CHAPTER III

The Knight Gregorius and the Lady Mother

Gregorius reaches his mother's country, obtains
sight of the liege lady, and serves her as knight
in the besieged city.

To Heaven now the exiled youth
Raised his hands and heart; in truth
Most fervently to God he prayed
For direction and for aid,
That to some land He'd let him sail
Where his voyage would avail.   1830
Thus his mariners he saw fit
To command: that they submit
To the course the winds designed,
And have the vessel follow blind,
As the winds chose to direct,*
And never from that course deflect.
Strong was the wind that rose and blew,
And with the wind the vessel flew.
A gale then in a few days more
Drove them to his mother's shore.   1840
Now as before I have related,
So scorched her land and devastated,
Nothing else was left his mother
Save her chief city, and no other;
And it too was besieged with might,
And by grief beset. The knight,
When he this city did discern,
Bade his mariners now turn

daz si dar wanten
die segelẹ und dâ lanten.   1850
  Dô die burgære sâhen
daz schef dort zuo gâhen,
dô sazten si sich mit her
disem scheffe ze wer.
nû zeictẹ in der ellende
vridelîche hende
und vrâcte die burgære
waz ir angest wære.
des nam si besunder
alle michel wunder,   1860
von wannen der herre
gevaren wære sô verre
daz er des niene weste.
ir einer der beste
undersagetẹ im vil gar,
als ich iu ê, waz in war.
als er ir nôt hete vernomen,
er sprach: 'sô bin ich rehte komen.
daz ist des ich got ie bat
daz er mich bræhte an die stat   1870
dâ ich ze tuonne vunde,
daz ich mîn junge stunde
niht müezic enlæge,
dâ man urliuges phlæge.
geruochet es diu vrouwe mîn,
ich wil gernẹ ir soldenære sîn.'
  Nû sâhen sị daz er wære
vil harte lobebære
an lîbe und an guote:
mit willigem muote   1880
wart er geherberget dô.
diu vrouwe was des gastes vrô:
doch hete sị in dannoch niht gesehen.
nû was im dar an wol geschehen:
den er ze wirte gewan,
der was ein harte vrum man,

And shift the sails, with the command
That on this shore they were to land.   1850
  Now when the people of the town
Saw the vessel speeding down,
Against this ship in their alarm
They took to arms to keep from harm.
The exile gestured that he meant
But well and was of peaceful bent.
He asked the townsmen to make clear
To him the reason for their fear.
Their amazement was untold
At his question; young and old   1860
Marveled most at what far land
The knight had come from to their strand
That he could be so unaware
And ignorant of this affair.
One noble of the town narrated
In detail what I've related
To you before. On having heard
About their plight, the knight averred:
"Then truly I've come here aright.
For I've prayed God both day and night   1870
That He direct me to a place
Where many deeds I could embrace,
And my young years not idly spend
While men in warfare did contend.
Should this my lady wish of me,
Her knight I now will gladly be."
  So praiseworthy did they find him,
For comely was his every limb,
And to such wealth he'd fallen heir,
They gladly gave him shelter there.   1880
The lady of the land was glad
About the guest, though yet she'd had
No sight of him. Now it chanced thus,
Most fortunate was Gregorius,
For happily he gained as host
A man who was of uttermost

der besten einer von der stat.
swaz er dem gebôt und bat,
daz vuor nâch sînem muote.
daz galt er wol mit guote.   1890
sîn zerunge was rîche
und doch sô bescheidenlîche
daz im dar under nie gebrast:
des wart er ein werder gast.

  Dô er vernam diu mære
daz diu vrouwe wære
schœne junc und âne man,
daz ir daz urliuge dar an
und diu ungenâde geschach
daz si den herzogen versprach   1900
und daz si ze stæte
die man versprochen hæte,
dô hæte er si gerne gesehen:
und wie daz möhte geschehen
âne missewende,
des vrâcte der ellende.
ouch was ir von im geseit
diu zuht und diu vrümikeit
daz ouch si in vil gerne sach.
daz selten gaste dâ geschach.   1910
wan daz was ir ellich site:
dâ erzeicte si mite
ir angestlîche swære
(wan ir was vreude unmære):
er wære arm oder rîch,
gast oder heimlîch,
den lie si sich niemer gesehen,
ez enmöhte ze münster geschehen,
dâ si stuont an ir gebete,
als si zallen zîten tete,   1920
ez benæme ir slâf oder maz.

  Nû riet der wirt dem gaste daz
daz er ir truhsæzen bat
daz er in bræhte an die stat

Integrity, one of the best
Within the city. Each request
Or bidding he fulfilled entire,
According to the knight's desire;   1890
And he was well repaid. Good sense
Was shown in all munificence.
No lack was ever manifest.
In high esteem he ranked as guest.
    When of the tale he grew aware
About the lady liege, so fair,
So young in years, and still unwed—
Of how she'd been besieged and led
To suffer such calamity,
Because she had refused to be   1900
The duke's wife, and of how she'd said
A mortal man she'd never wed—
He wished to see her; and he now,
Stranger that he was, asked how
That might take place without offense.
    Meanwhile when his excellence
Of breeding and good character
Had also been described to her,
She greatly wished to see him, too,
Though rare it was that she would view   1910
A guest; for ordinarily
(Towards joy she felt such apathy),
She made her grief in this way clear:
Before no guest would she appear—
Whether rich or poor he be,
No matter what his pedigree,
Whether acquainted with her or
A stranger to her—she forbore—
Except at the cathedral where
She'd always stand* engrossed in prayer   1920
Though she would thus lack sleep and food.
    The host in all solicitude
Advised his guest now to appeal
To her lord steward to reveal

dâ er si möhte gesehen.
daz lie der truhsæze geschehen.
er nam in eines tages sît
vruo in einer messezît
und vuorte in an sîner hant
dâ er si an ir gebete vant   1930
und lie in si wol beschouwen.
der truhsæze sprach zer vrouwen:
'vrouwe, grüezet disen man,
wande er iu wol gedienen kan.'
vür einen gast enphie si ir kint:
ouch was sîn herze dar an blint
und im unkunt genuoc
daz in diu selbe vrouwe truoc.
    Nû sach si in ze vlîze an
und mê dan si deheinen man   1940
vordes ie getæte:
daz kam von sîner wæte.
dô si die rehte besach,
wider sich selben si des jach,
daz daz sîdîn gewant
daz si mit ir selber hant
zuo ir kinde hete geleit
unde disse gastes kleit
gelîche wæren begarwe
der güete und der varwe: 1950
ez wære benamen daz selbe gewant,
oder daz si von einer hant
geworht wæren beide.
daz ermande si ir leide.
nu behagete im diu vrouwe wol
als einem manne ein wip sol
an der nihtes gebrast:
ouch behagete ir der gast
baz danne ie man getæte.
daz macheten sîne ræte   1960
der ouch vroun Êven verriet,
dô si von gotes gebote schiet.

Where he could obtain sight of her.
The steward agreed without demur.
He took him one day afterward
To early mass then being heard,
And led him by the hand to where
The lady liege was found at prayer,   1930
And let him feast his eye on her.
"My lady, on this man confer
Your welcome," the lord steward said,
"For he can serve you in good stead."
Her child as stranger she did greet.
And blind his heart was as it beat
For the lady, unaware
That she had borne him who stood there.
    She looked at him attentively
And on him gazed longer than she   1940
On any man had gazed before;
The reason was the clothes he wore.*
As she with care noted his dress,
To herself she did confess:
The silken fabrics and brocade
That she with her own hand had laid
Beside her child, and those that clad
This foreign stranger surely had
The selfsame hue and quality.
Indeed, it was most certainly   1950
The very same material—
Or else, once the identical,
Skilled hand had woven both. The sight
Recalled to her her grievous plight.
Now as a woman who lacks naught
Will please a man, as well she ought,
The lady liege pleased him; and he,
The stranger, pleased her more than she
Had ever before been pleased by man.
This was achieved by him whose plan   1960
Corrupted Lady Eve when she
Also strayed from God's decree.

Sus bevalh in diu guote
ins truhsæzen huote
unde schieden sich sâ.
sîn herze lie er bî ir dâ
und vleiz sich deste mêre
ûf prîs und ûf êre,
daz er si hâte gesehen.
im was sô liebe dran geschehen   1970
daz er sich dûhte vreuderîch.

nû vant man aller tägelîch
ritterschaft vor der stat,
swie des mannes herze bat,
zorse und ze vuoze.
daz was sîn unmuoze.
des wart er schiere mære:
swenne die burgære
an die vîende kâmen,
swelhen schaden si dâ nâmen,   1980
sô vergie in selten daz
er engetæte ie etewaz
dâ von er wart ze schalle
und ze prîse vür si alle.
    Daz treip er unz ûf die stunde
daz er wesen kunde
ritter swie man gerte,
ze sper und ze swerte.
als er die kunst vil gar bevant
tägelichen mit der hant   1990
und er benamen weste
daz er wære der beste
(er hete ellen unde kraft
und ganze kunst ze ritterschaft),
dô êrste wart sîn vrävele grôz.
wie lützel in der nôt verdrôz!

Entrusting him unto the care
Of her lord steward, then and there,
The gracious lady did depart,
But with her that day went his heart.
Now that he'd seen her face to face,
To fame and glory he gave chase
All the more, with growing zeal:
Such happiness he'd come to feel;   1970
Life's joys were richly his, he thought.

> Gregorius gains renown as a knight and van-
> quishes the formidable duke in single combat.

Outside the walls the knights now sought
To vie on foot or on a steed,
Each day in tournaments, indeed,
Such as men's hearts do long to see.
Devoting himself eagerly
To jousting, he soon gained renown.
Often as men from the town
Went forth against the enemy,
Whatever losses there might be,   1980
Rare was the day he'd not compete
And on the field perform some feat
That merited him glory and
Acclaim above all in the land.
To do this he continued till
He had developed every skill
Required of an able knight
Who used his spear and sword aright.
On fully mastering the art
By daily practice on his part,   1990
Increasing his dexterity
Until he knew himself to be
The best of all the knights, at length
(He had the spirit, skill, and strength
That knighthood needs) he waxed bold, never
Minding toil and effort—ever

er was der vîende hagel,
an jagen ein houbet, an vluht ein zagel.
  Nû was der Rômære
von sîner manheit mære,   2000
der herzoge der in daz lant
hete verhert und verbrant,
vil sterker dannę ein ander man.
ouch was dem selben dar an
sô schône gelungen
daz er mit gemeiner zungen
zem besten ritter wart genant
über älliu diu lant.
nû was daz sîn gewonheit
daz er eine dicke reit   2010
durch justieren vür daz tor.
dâ tet erz ritterlichen vor:
wande swelh ritter guot
durch sînen ritterlîchen muot
her ûz justierte wider in,
den vuortę er ie gevangen hin
zer burgære gesihte
und envorhte si ze nihte.
des hetę er alles vil getriben
daz in niemen was beliben   2020
der in bestüende mêre:
doch versuochtę erz dicke sêre.
  Nu erschamte sich Grêgôrjus,
daz in ein man alsus
hete geleit ein michel her
âne aller slahte wer.
dô gedâhtę er dicke dar an:
'nû sihę ich dicke daz ein man
der zabel sêre minnet,
swennę er daz guot gewinnet   2030
daz er ûf zabel wâgen wil,
vindet er dannę ein glîchez spil,
sô dunket er sich harte rîch:
und istz joch ein teil ungelîch,

First in pursuit, last in retreat—
His foe's undoing and defeat.
 Now famed for courage was that Roman,*
The duke, the liege lady's fierce foeman,   2000
Who had overrun her land
And devastated it with brand;
No man was mightier than he.
In jousting so remarkably
Had he success and victory scored,
Small wonder that with one accord
Throughout the land he'd been acclaimed
And foremost of all knights been named.
It was his custom to advance
Alone to combat with his lance   2010
Before the walls outside the gate.
His gallantry there waxed so great,
Regardless who the valiant knight
That ventured forth with him to fight
For the sake of chivalry,
The duke would lead him, fearlessly
Before the people's very eyes,
Away with him as captive prize.
So often had he victory gained,
Presently no one remained   2020
Who dared oppose him; yet would he
Challenge them quite frequently.
 Gregorius now felt mortified
That thus a single man had vied
And laid a mighty army low
With no resistance from his foe.
Quite often then his thought would be:
"Now this I've seen repeatedly:
The man who dearly loves to bet
Upon the board thinks he will net   2030
Most happily a double gain
If first the funds he can obtain
To gamble with, and secondly
He finds the players' bets must be

er bestâtz ûf einen guoten val.
nû hân ich eines spiles wal.
bin et ich sô wol gemuot
daz ich mîn vil armez guot
wâge wider sô rîche habe,
daz ich iemer dar abe   2040
gêret und gerîchet bin,
ob mir gevallet der gewin.
ich bin ein ungelobeter man
und verzagete noch nie dar an,
ich engedenke dar nâch alle tage,
wie ich die sælde bejage
daz ich ze vollem lobe gestê.
nu enweiz ich niht wie daz ergê:
ich enwâge drumbe den lîp,
man hât mich iemer vür ein wîp   2050
und bin der êren betrogen.
mac ich nû disen herzogen
ûf gotes gnâde bestân?
nû weiz ich doch wol daz ich hân
beidiu sterke und den muot.
ich wil benamen diz arme guot
wâgen ûf disem spil.
man klaget mich niht ze vil,
ob ich von im tôt gelige:
ist aber daz ich im an gesige,   2060
sô bin ich êren rîche
iemer êwiclîche.
daz wizze man unde wîp,
mir ist lieber daz mîn lîp
bescheidenlîchẹ ein ende gebe
dan daz ich lasterlichen lebe.'
    Grêgôrjus sichs vil gar bewac
daz er ez deheinen tac
wolde vristen mêre:
durch got und durch êre   2070
woldẹ er verliesen sînen lîp
oder daz unschuldige wîp

Laid even. Yet although the stakes
May be uneven, still he takes
A gamble on a lucky throw.
With me now rests the choice to show
Whether I'm brave enough to take
This risk; my paltry life to stake   2040
Against the odds of precious gain;
For if I win I'll thus attain
Henceforth to glory, wealth, and fame.
    "Though to renown I have no claim,
I've daily pondered on this theme
Of how the bliss of men's esteem
I'd best obtain. What now will be
The outcome, I can not forsee;
But if this trial I'll not endeavor
A woman I'll be thought forever;   2050
Prestige and fame I'll be denied.
But if on God's grace I relied,
Could I succeed in an attack
Now on the duke? I have no lack
Of strength or courage—that I know!
Yes! I will stake upon one throw
This, my paltry life and breath;
And if at his hand I meet death,
People will not greatly mourn.
But if by me from life he's torn,   2060
Victorious I would be, forever
Rich in honor. Let men never
Think otherwise than thus of me:
I'd rather meet death fittingly,
Live briefly but with honor graced,
Than live a longer life abased."
    Gregorius resolved no day
Would he longer now delay;
For he was ready to lay down
His life for God and great renown,   2070
Or else in this way liberate
The innocent lady from her state

lœsen von des herren hant
der ir genomen hâtẹ ir lant.
diz sagetẹ er niuwan einem man
der in mohte wol dar an
gevrumen und gewerren,
dem oberisten herren:
er woldez nieman mêre sagen.
morgen dôz begunde tagen, 2080
dô hôrtẹ er eine messe vruo
und bereite sich dar zuo
als er ze velde wolde komen.
der wirt wart zuo der rede genomen:
der half im ûz vür die stat.
mit grôzem vlîzẹ er in des bat
daz er des war næme,
swennẹ er wider kæme,
daz er in lieze wider in,
er bræhte verlust oder gewin. 2090
  Alsus kam der guote
mit manlîchem muote
geriten über jenez velt
vür des herzogen gezelt,
dâ er in inne weste.
nu ersach in der muotveste
unde wâfente sich sâ
und ouch nieman mêre dâ.
alle die er dâ hâte
die ruoften daz man drâte 2100
im sîn ors gewünne:
er vorhte daz er im entrünne.
als in Grêgôrjus komen sach,
vil sinneclichen im geschach.
er begunde im entwîchen
vil harte kärclîchen
zuo den sînen vür daz tor.
vil wol erbeitẹ er sîn dâ vor,
ob er in bekumbern möhte,
daz im niene töhte 2110

Of subjugation at the hand
Of the lord who'd seized her land.
To no one but a single Man
Did Gregory now reveal his plan—
To One alone, the Supreme Lord,
Who help or hindrance could accord—
In no one else would he confide.
Now when the light with darkness vied,   2080
At dawn, to early mass he went,*
Preparing for the day's event
As one who rides afield to joust.
His host, when drawn into his trust,
Helped him through the city gate.
He implored the man to wait,
And watch for him with all concern,
And let him in on his return,
No matter whether it should be
He brought defeat or victory.   2090
    With manly spirit thus the knight
Rode at a gallop out of sight
Across the field, and straightway went
Cantering before the tent
In which he knew the duke to be.
The fearless duke immediately,
On seeing him, seized arms alone
(Thus deference to him was shown).*
All near him cried out that his steed
Be quickly brought him, for indeed   2100
He feared the mounted knight might flee.
    Gregorius, on the contrary,
When he saw him in pursuit,
A sly maneuver did execute;
Evading his foe's charge instead,
By slow retreat the duke he led
Toward his people before the gate.
There he halted to await
The duke, whom he wished to reduce
To such sore straits that of no use   2110

diu helfe von sînem her.
nû saz diu burcmûrę und diu wer
vol ritter unde vrouwen
die daz wolden schouwen
wederm dâ gelunge.
nu ensûmte sich niht der junge.
    Ir ietweder sich dâ vleiz
ûf einen langen puneiz.
zuo ein ander wart in ger.
alse schiere si diu sper   2120
under die arme sluogen,
diu ors si zesamene truogen.
diu sper wâren kurz und grôz,
des ir ietweder missenôz:
wandę ir ietweder stach
daz sîn daz ez ze stücken brach
und daz si doch gesâzen.
wie lützel si vergâzen
der swerte bî der sîten!
seht, si begunden strîten,   2130
zwêne gelîche starke man
der enweder nie gewan
unredelîche zageheit
(daz sî iu vür wâr geseit)
alse grôz als umbę ein hâr,
und ez muose dâ vür wâr
den strît under in beiden
kunst und gelücke scheiden.
    Dô ir ietweder gnuoc
mit dem swerte gesluoc,   2140
dô bekumbertę in alsus
der getühtige Grêgôrjus
daz er in zoumen began
und vuortę in mit gewalte dan
vaste gegen dem bürgetor.
daz was im noch beslozzen vor
und enwart niht drâte in verlân.
nû hâte des war getân

Would be the help of his armed men.
Both knights and ladies crowded then
The wall and ramparts of the town,
Eager to know as they looked down
Which of the two would win; in truth,
No time was lost by the brave youth.

    Apart a goodly distance, both
Prepared for a long charge. Not loath
Were they to make an onset; and
No sooner had each made his stand   2120
And pressed his spear with utmost speed
Beneath his arm, than each one's steed
Went rushing at the other. Vain
Their first encounter! for the twain
Had short and heavy spears that broke
Asunder as each made his stroke:
Yet horsed and seated both remained
Despite the impact. As they reined
Their steeds, no moment did they waste
But drew their swords. Lo! as they faced   2130
For combat they were equal both
In strength and power; now on my oath,
Neither one of them did show
The merest breath—and this I know—
Of base timidity. Unknown
To each was cowardice. Alone
Their skill, and chance, had to decree
Who now should gain the victory.

    When sword in hand, they both had fought
At length, Gregorius so brought   2140
The duke to sore distress that he,
With valor and dexterity,
Seized the bridle of the horse
And led the captive duke with force
Off to the gate with him straightway;
Still locked, it caused him some delay
Before he gained admission there.
The ducal knights, of this aware,

des herzogen ritterschaft.
die begunden mit aller ir kraft   2150
gegen ir herren gâhen.
dô daz die burgære sâhen,
dô wurfen si ûf diu bürgetor.
alsus ergie dâ vor
der aller hertiste strît
der vordes oder sît
von sô vil liuten ergie.
doch behabete Grêgôrjus hie
sînen gevangenen man
und brâhte in ritterlichen dan.   2160
zuo sluogen si diu bürgetor.
dô huoben si dâ vor
einen sturm harte grôz:
unlanc was daz sis verdrôz.
  Der sælige Grêgôrjus
der bejagete im alsus
des tages michel êre
und hete von grôzem sêre
erlœset sîner muoter lant
mit sîner ellenthaften hant.   2170
vordes was sîn prîs sô grôz
daz niemen vrumen des verdrôz
er enspræche sîn êre:
nû hât er ir aber mêre.
ouch hât diu vrouwe und ir lant
von sîner gehülfigen hant
alle ir nôt überkomen.
swaz si schaden hete genomen,
der wart ir volleclîche ersat,
als si gebôt unde bat,   2180
und emphie des rehte sicherheit
daz er ir dehein leit
vürdermâl getæte.
daz liez er harte stæte.

Since they their lord's plight did perceive,
With all their might sped to relieve   2150
Their liege. The people of the town,
As from the ramparts they looked down,
Beheld this, and made wide the gate.
The tide of battle could not wait:
No fiercer fighting ever ensued
Among so great a multitude.
But Gregorius in the fray,
Keeping the captive, did display
True knightliness, as with him then
He rode inside the town again.   2160
The gate was closed without delay,
And those who stood outside straightway
Stormed furiously; but soon they grew
Aweary of it, and withdrew.
    And so Gregorius in this way,
Happy man, gained through that day
Great fame, for with his manly hand
He had set free his mother's land,
And by his prowess gallantly
Redeemed it from great misery.   2170
Prior to this day his name
Already had won such acclaim
That no one grudged him praise, but how
He was extolled and lauded now!
Also, through his helping hand
The realm and lady of the land
Recovered from their harsh privation.
She obtained full reparation
For every loss, and all that she
Demanded of her enemy   2180
The duke now promised to concede.
He under solemn oath agreed
To do her no more injury,
And steadfast to his word was he.

Dô diz nœtige lant
sînen kumber überwant
und mit vride stuont als ê,
nû tet den lantherren wê
diu tägelîche vorhte
die in der zwîvel worhte   2190
daz ez in sam müese ergân,
ob si aber wolde bestân
dehein gewaltigiu hant.
si sprachen, ez wærez grôze lant
mit einem wîbe unbewart
vor unrehter hôchvart
'und hete wir einen herren,
so enmöhte uns niht gewerren.'
    Nû wurden si alsô drâte
under in ze râte   2200
daz si die vrouwen bæten
und daz mit vlîze tæten
daz si einen man næme
der in ze herren gezæme:
daz wære in allen enden guot.
si westen wol daz si den muot
ir durch got hæte erkorn
daz si hæte verborn
und verberen wolde alle man.
dâ missetæte si an: 2210
ir leben wære übele bewant,
ob si ein sô rîchez lant
ir dankes âne erben
sus wolde verderben.
diz wæren ir ræte
daz si noch baz tæte
wider die werlt und wider got
(si behielte so baz sîn gebot)

Peace comes to the realm. The nobles persuade
their liege lady to take a husband. She weds
Gregorius who becomes an excellent ruler.

Now when this harried realm had shed
Its sore afflictions and there spread
Upon the land sweet peace again,
A fear arose among the men
Of noble rank as day by day
Uncertainty caused them dismay   2190
At thought that they might undergo
A like disaster, should a foe
Attack them mightily. They said,
With a woman as their head,
Open lay their widespread lands
To lawless and presumptuous hands;
"But if a man ruled over us,
Safe, we'd not be troubled thus."
  Among themselves they speedily
Took counsel and did all agree   2200
That they would steadfastly implore
And beg their lady to set store
By their request and choose to wed
A husband fit to be their head.
In all respects would that be good.
Well they knew and understood
That she no husband wished to take,
Since she'd renounced men for God's sake.
Her conduct, they said, was amiss,
And she was doing wrong in this,   2210
Putting her life to no good use
If she'd so great a realm reduce
To naught, by willing to forbear
From giving birth to any heir.
These were the thoughts they weighed in mind:
In God's sight and before mankind
Far better would she lead her life
To choose a man and be his wife

daz si einen man næme
und erben bekæme. 2220
diz was benamen der beste rât:
wande êlich hîrât
daz ist daz aller beste leben
daz got der werlde hât gegeben.

Dô ir der rehten wârheit
alsô vil wart vür geleit,
si volgete ir râte und ir bete
alsô daz siz in gote tete
und gelobete ze nemen einen man.
da geschach ir aller wille an. 2230
nû rieten si über al
daz man ir lieze die wal
ze nemen swen si wolde.
dô daz wesen solde,
do gedâhte diu guote
vil dicke in ir muote
wen si nemen möhte
der baz ir muote töhte
danne den selben man
(und geviel vil gar dar an) 2240
den ir got hete gesant
ze lœsen si und ir lant.
daz was ir sun Grêgôrjus.
dar nâch wart er alsus
vil schiere sîner muoter man.
da ergie des tiuvels wille an.

Dô si den herren sagete
wer ir dar zuo behagete,
nû wâren si niemans alsô vrô:
ze herren nâmen si in dô. 2250
ez enwart nie wünne merre
dan diu vrouwe und der herre
mit ein ander hâten,
wan si wâren berâten
mit liebe in grôzen triuwen;
seht, daz ergie mit riuwen.

And bring forth heirs (she would obey
God's Laws far better in this way).   2220
No wiser counsel could there be.
For lawful wedlock, certainly,
Of all lives since the world began
Is the best life God gave to man.
   When they to her had thus appealed,
And the true state of things revealed,
To do God's will, she then complied
With their requests and testified
A husband she would now acquire,
Fulfilling, thus, all their desire.   2230
Now they were of a single voice,
Declaring she should have the choice
Of whom she was to marry. Then,
Since marry she must, time and again
The thought would enter in her mind,
What better husband could she find
Who'd be more fitting than that knight
Whom God had sent her in her plight,
Who had not only freed her land,
But rescued her from the duke's hand.   2240
This thought she grew now to prefer,
Such was its strong appeal to her.
It was Gregorius, the same
Who was her son, that soon became
His mother's husband in this way.
In that the Devil had the say.
   When to her nobles she did avow
Whom she pleased to marry now,
More gratified they could not be,
And made him liege immediately.   2250
Never was there more delight
Than that felt by the lordly knight
With his lady, for the two
In deep devotion sweet love knew
And sought each other's company.
But, lo, this ended ruefully.

er was guot rihtære,
von sîner milte mære.
swaz einem manne mac gegeben
zer werlde ein wünneclîchez leben,   2260
des hâte er gar des wunsches wal:
daz nam einen gæhen val.
    Sîn lant und sîne marke
die bevridete er alsô starke,
swer si mit arge ruorte
daz er den zevuorte
der êren und des guotes.
er was vestes muotes:
enhæte erz niht durch got verlân,
im müesen wesen undertân   2270
swaz im der lande was gelegen.
nû wolde aber er der mâze phlegen:
durch die gotes êre
so engerte er nihtes mêre
wan daz im dienen solde:
vürbaz er niene wolde.

    Die tavel hâte er alle wege
in sîner heimlîchen phlege
verborgen ûf sîner veste,
dâ die niemen weste,   2280
diu dâ bî im vunden was.
an der er tägelichen las
sîn sündeclîche sache
den ougen zungemache,
wie er geboren würde
und die süntlîche bürde
sîner muoter und sînes vater.
unsern herren got bater
in beiden umbe hulde
und erkande niht der schulde   2290
diu ûf sîn selbes rücke lac,

As sovereign he well ruled the land,
Renowned for his most generous hand.
He had at his command the choice
Of everything that can rejoice   2260
Man's life on earth and him enthrall.
All this came to a sudden fall.

His borders and his whole country
He'd fortified to such degree,
He easily did overwhelm
Whoever would attack his realm;
And every foe he did contrive
Of wealth and honor to deprive.
So resolute was he, perforce,
If he had not renounced his course   2270
For love of God, each neighboring land
He'd have reduced to his command.
Since moderation he desired,
And to God's glory he aspired,*
Nothing further wished that knight
But what was duly his by right.

A servant maid betrays Gregorius' secret grief.

Within his stronghold well concealed
In his own care, to none revealed,
He always kept the tablet safe—
The one found on the infant waif—   2280
Of its existence no one knew.
Tears filled his eyes; doleful he grew
As he read daily with sad glance
Of how in sinful circumstance
He had been born, and weeping read
Of what parents he was bred,
Who both were burdened with such sin.
Then in prayer he would begin
To beg the Lord that He bestow
His grace on them. He did not know   2290
Or recognize in any way

die er naht unde tac
mit sîner muoter uopte,
dâ mitẹ er got betruopte.

   Nû was dâ ze hovẹ ein maget,
alsô karc, sô man saget,
diu verstuont sich sîner klage wol,
als ich iu nû sagen sol,
wan si der kemenâten phlac,
dâ diu tavel inne lac: 2300
er hete genomen ze sîner klage
ie ein zît in dem tage
die er ouch niemer versaz.
nu gemarhte diu juncvrouwe daz,
swenne sị in dar in verlie,
daz er dar lachende gie
und schiet ie als ein riuwic man
mit rôten ougen dan.

   Nû vleiz si sich iemer mêre
herzelichen sêre   2310
wie si daz rehtẹ ersæhe
wâ von diụ klage geschæhe
und sleich im eines tages mite,
dô er aber nâch sînem site
ze kemenâten klagen gie.
dô was diu juncvrouwe hie
und barc sich unz daz si gesach
sînen klägelîchen ungemach
und daz er an der tavel las,
alse sîn gewonheit was.   2320
dô er des harte vil getete
mit weinen unde mit gebete,
dô truckentẹ er diu ougen
und wânde sîniu tougen
vor al der werlde wol bewarn.
nû hetez diu maget alsus ervarn:
war er die tavel leite,
daz ersach si vil gereite.

The guilt that rested night and day
On him, as with his mother he,
To God's offense, lived sinfully.
    At court now, so the tale is told,
There lived a servant maid, so bold
And shrewd that she soon found the clue
To his sorrow, as I'll tell you:
That very room she cleaned and swept
Where he the little tablet kept.   2300
Now he a certain time each day,
Without fail, without delay,
Had set aside for his lament.
The young maid marked he always went
Smiling into the room—his mien,
As she would let him in, serene;
With reddened eyes he left that room,
A man of sorrow and of gloom.
    Now she did stealthily endeavor,
With growing zeal that ceased not ever,   2310
The true cause to ascertain
Of his mourning and his pain.
She slyly followed him one day,
While once again he made his way
Into that chamber to lament,
As was his custom. In she went
And stayed concealed in a recess
And watched his pitiful distress
While he read the tablet through,
As he was always wont to do.   2320
Now after he had often read
What the little tablet said,
With tears and prayers, his eyes he dried,
Convinced that what he had to hide
Was known to none. Yet in this way
The maid learned quickly where now lay
The tablet he had kept concealed:
Its hiding place was now revealed.

Dô sîn klagę ein ende nam,
diu maget vil harte schiere kam   2330
zuo ir vrouwen unde sprach:
'vrouwe, waz ist der ungemach
dâ von mîn herre trûret sô,
daz ir mit im niht sît unvrô?'
diu vrouwe sprach: 'waz meinestû?
jâ schiet er niuwelichen nû
von uns vil vrœlichen hie:
waz möhtę er, sît er von mir gie,
vernomen hân der mære
dâ von er trûric wære?   2340
wærę im solhes iht gesaget,
daz enhete er mich niht verdaget.
im enist ze weinen niht geschehen:
dû hâst entriuwen missesehen.'
'vrouwe, leider ich enhân.
dêswâr ich sach in hiute stân
dâ in ein riuwe gevie
diu mir an mîn herze gie.'
'Sich, jâ was ez ie dîn site
unde hâst mir dâ mite   2350
gemachet manige swære,
du engesagetest nie guot mære.
noch baz dû gedagetest
dan dû die lüge sagetest
diu mir ze schaden gezüge.'
'vrouwe, diz ist niht ein lüge.
jâ enist anders niht min klage
wan daz ich iu sô wâr sage.'
'sich, sô meinestûz doch sô?'
'entriuwen jâ, er ist unvrô.   2360
ich wândę ir∙westetz michel baz.
jâ vrouwe, waz mac wesen daz
daz er vor iu sô gar verstilt,
wan er iuch anders niht enhilt?
zewâre, vrouwe, swaz ez sî,
im wonet ein grôziu swære bî.

Scarcely had his sad lament
Come to an end, when off she went   2330
With haste, and maid to mistress said,
"What trouble, lady, has so led
My lord to mourn without relief,
And you not sharing in his grief?"
The lady spoke: "What do you mean?
Just now he went away serene,
And left us here so cheerfully.
Now while he has been gone from me
What tidings could have reached his ear
To make his joy quite disappear?   2340
If grievous news he had been told,
Such news from me he'd not withhold.
He's had no cause such tears to shed;
In what you saw, you were misled."
"Lady, alas, that is not so!
Today I saw him sunk in woe.
With such sorrow was he stricken
That at the sight my heart did sicken."
    "Look, now, good news you've never brought,
But evil news you've ever sought,   2350
As your fixed habit, to impart,
And always vexed me much at heart.
Far better silent to remain
Than such a lie here to maintain
That could be to my injury."
"Lady, no lie you hear from me.
What I regret most telling you
Is this: all that I say is true."
"You mean that this is really so?"
"He's truly sad; this you would know,   2360
I thought, better than I. Indeed,
What can it be that he would need
So to conceal it from your view,
When nothing else he keeps from you?
My lady, be it what it may,
He suffers greatly; I must say

ich hâns ouch mê war genomen:
nû bin ichs an ein ende komen
daz er sô grôzen kumber treit
den er noch nieman hât geseit.   2370
sît er hie disses landes phlac,
so enlie er nie deheinen tac
er giengę ie wider morgen
eine und verborgen
in die kemenâten,
vreude wol berâten:
swie vrœlich er dar in gie,
sô schiet er doch ze jungist ie
her ûz vil harte riuwevar.
doch genam ichs nie sô rehte war   2380
als ich hiute hân getân.
dô ich in sach dar in gân,
dô stal ich mich mit im dar in
und barc mich dâ unz daz ich in
und alle sîn gebærdę ersach.
ich sach in grôzen ungemach
von unmanlîcher klage begân
unde vor ime hân
ein dinc dâ an geschriben was:
dô er daz sach unde las,   2390
sô sluoc er sich zen brüsten ie
und bôt sich an sîniu knie
mit venjen vil dicke,
mit manigem ûfblicke.
ich gesach joch nieman mêre
geweinen alsô sêre.
dâ bî erkandę ich harte wol
daz sîn herzę ist leides vol:
wan dâ enzwîvel ich niht an
umbę einen sô geherzen man,   2400
swâ dem ze weinenne geschiht,
daz ist âne herzeriuwe niht,
als ich in hiute weinen sach.'
   Diu vrouwe trûriclichen sprach:

I'd noticed it before, of course,
But now I've traced it to the source.
This deep grief that he bears concealed
He has to no one yet revealed.   2370
  "Ever since he first held sway
In our realm, there's been no day
That he's not risen with the dawn
Alone, and secretly withdrawn
In good spirits to this room;
But he'd depart from it in gloom.
No matter with what cheerful mien
He'd come, at length, far from serene,
And sorrowing he'd go away.
At no time until today   2380
Had I with care observed it so.
When to that room I saw him go,
In I stole with him and hid,
Till I had witnessed all he did.
And as I stayed in there concealed,
His great disquiet he revealed,
In unmanly loud outcries.
I saw him hold before his eyes
A thing inscribed that he'd proceed
To gaze upon and ever read.   2390
His breast he did not cease to beat*
In grief, and on his knees entreat
In fervent prayer Our Dear Lord's love,
With many a glance to Heaven above.
I'd never seen a man before
Weep so bitterly and sore.
That his heart is full of pain,
Thus to me became quite plain.
For I can have no doubt at all,
When such a valiant man falls thrall   2400
To weeping, and he so gives way
As I, myself, saw him today,
He surely suffers heartfelt pain."
  The mistress spoke in this sad vein:

'ouwê mîns lieben herren!
waz mac im danne werren?
mir ist sîns kumbers niht mê kunt:
wan er ist junc und gesunt
und rîch ze guoter mâze.
dar zuo ich niene lâze   2410
ich envâre sîns willen als ich sol.
dêswâr des mac mich lüsten wol,
wandę er daz wol verschulden kan.
hât dehein wîp tiurern man,
dêswâr daz lâzę ich âne zorn:
wandę er enwart weizgot nie geborn.
ouwê mir armen wîbe!
ja engeschach mînem lîbe
nie deheiner slahte guot
und ouch niemer getuot   2420
niuwan von sîn eines tugent.
nû waz mac im ze sîner jugent
sô vil ze weinenne sîn geschehen
als ich dich dâ hœre jehen?
nû tuo mir etelîchen rât,
sît daz er michz verswigen hât,
wie ich sîn leit ervar
daz ich mich doch an im bewar.
ich vürhtę, ob ich mirz sagen bite,
ich verliese in dâ mite.   2430
ich weiz wol, swelh sache
im ze leidę oder zungemache
geschæhe diu ze sagennę ist,
die enverswigę er mich deheine vrist.
nu enger ich doch dehein geschiht
wider sînen willen ze wizzen niht,
wan daz mir diz durch einen list
alsô nôt ze wizzennę ist,
ob sîner swære
iender alsô wære   2440
daz im mîn helfe töhte
und im sị benemen möhte.

"Alas, my lord! What can it be
That troubles him so dreadfully?
Not till this moment did I know
That anything disturbed him so!
For he has health and wealth and youth;
His will I never fail, in truth,   2410
To do, as is most meet for me.
I do this for him happily:
He merits and requites it well.
A better husband it befell
No wife to have. God knows, I scorn
The thought that better e'er was born.
Alas, poor me, good luck has never
In all my life, nor will it ever,
Come my way, and I have known
No luck, except through him alone—   2420
His goodness and his manliness.
What can have happened to distress
Him so much in his youth that he
Must weep as you've been telling me?
But since he's kept this from me, pray,
Give me some counsel how I may
Discover why he suffers so;
Yet let me not his love forgo.
If I ask him to make all clear,
He will be lost to me, I fear.   2430
What sorrow or distress he'd feel,
Such grief from me he'd not conceal,
And talk with me he surely would,
I know, if it were to some good.
What may have happened of concern
To him I do not wish to learn
Against his will, save that I need
To know for this good cause: indeed,
If once I knew, I then might be
Of use to him and readily   2440
Perhaps help him obtain relief,
Or in some way free him of grief.

daz er mich ie dehein geschiht,
si züge ze vreuden oder niht,
verswige, des was ich ungewon
und bin wol gewis dâ von
daz er mir diz ungerne saget.'
   'Nû râtę ich iu wol', sprach diu maget,
'daz irz harte wol ervart
und doch sîn hulde bewart.   2450
dâ ich in dâ stânde sach
klagende sînen ungemach,
die stat die marhtę ich harte wol,
als ich si iu zeigen sol.
dô er geweinde genuoc
und sich zen brüsten gesluoc,
daz er dâ vor im hâte
daz barc er alsô drâte
in ein mûrloch über sich.
die selben stat die marhte ich.   2460
muget ir des erbîten
(er wil doch birsen rîten),
vrouwe, sô vüerę ich iuch dar
und zeigez iu: sô nemet ir war
waz dar an geschriben sî,
dâ erkennet ir ez bî.
ez enist niht âne daz,
dar an enstê etewaz
geschriben von sînen sorgen
die er sus hât verborgen.'   2470

   Dô er nâch sîner gewonheit
ze walde birsen gereit,
dô tet si alsô drâte
nach der mägede râte
und gie dâ si die tavel vant
und erkande si zehant

That he should keep a thing from me,
Pleasant or not, as it may be,
Is what I'm not accustomed to.
That makes me certain in my view
That he is loath to tell it me."
    The maid said, "My advice would be,
The matter to its cause to trace
And yet remain in his good grace.   2450
I marked the spot where him I spied
As standing there he loudly cried,
Lamenting what distressed him so.
This very spot to you I'll show.
A long time passed while tears he wept
And beat his breast; the thing he'd kept
Before him in his hands, with haste
He lifted up on high and placed
Inside a hole within the wall.
I noted, too, this opening small.   2460
My lady, should you care to bide
Your time (for he plans soon to ride
To hunt), I'll lead you there and show
The thing to you; then you will know,
By reading what is written there,
The reason for his deep despair.
It can't be otherwise, it's plain,
Than that the reason for his pain
Is written on that thing, revealing
What he's been carefully concealing."   2470

        The liege lady discovers the tablet and reveals
        to Gregorius that she is his mother.

    Now when according to his wont
He'd ridden to the woods to hunt,
She straightway took her maid's advice
And acted on it in a trice.
She hurried to his room and drew
The tablet from the wall, and knew

daz ez diu selbe wære,
als man iu an dem mære
ouch dâ vor seite,
die si zir kinde leite.   2480
und als si dar an gelas
daz si aber versenket was
in den vil tiefen ünden
tœtlîcher sünden,
dô dûhte si sich unsælic gnuoc.
zuo den brüsten si sich sluoc
und brach ûz ir schœne hâr.
si gedâhte daz si vür wâr
zuo der helle wære geborn
und got hæte verkorn   2490
ir herzenlîchez riuwen
daz si begienc mit triuwen
umbe ir erren missetât,
als man iu ê gesaget hât,
sît er des tiuvels râte
nû aber verhenget hâte
daz si an der sünden grunt
was gevallen anderstunt.
    Ir vreuden sunne wart bedaht
mit tôtvinsterre naht.   2500
ich wæne ir herze wære
gebrochen von der swære,
wan daz ein kurz gedinge
ir muot tete ringe
und stuont ir trôst doch gar dar an.
si gedâhte: 'waz ob mînem man
disiu tavel ist zuo brâht
anders danne ich hân gedâht?
ob got mînen sun gesande
gesunden ze lande,   2510
etewer der in dâ vant
der hât tavel undz gewant
mînem herren ze koufen geben.
des gedingen wil ich leben,

At once it was the very one
She'd placed beside her infant son—
The tablet mentioned, as you know,
In this tale some time ago. 2480
And as the knowledge in her surged
That she was once again submerged
Beneath the waters and within
The darkling waves of deadly sin,
More than wretched and distraught
She beat her breast and ever sought
To tear out her beauteous hair.
Nor could she from the thought forbear
That for Hell she had been born,
And that God did truly scorn 2490
Her heartfelt penance and remorse
That for her erring, sinful course
She'd undergone (as has before
Been told to you), since now once more
The Lord had for a second time
Consented to the Devil's crime
And let her fall again within
The deep abyss of human sin.
  Now was the sun of her delight
Gone down in deadly black of night. 2500
Grief surely would have caused her heart
To break at once beneath the smart,
I do believe, had she not eased
Her mind with one faint hope and seized
Her only comfort in this thought:
"What if this tablet once was brought
To my dear husband otherwise
Than I was first drawn to surmise?
God may have let my son come safe
To shore, and he who found the waif 2510
Within the little boat then sold
Unto my lord, for precious gold,
The tablet and the raiment, both.
This will I hope and not be loath

unz ich die rede rehte ervar.'
ein bote wart gewunnen dar
und besande alsô balde
ir herren dâ ze walde.

Der bote gâhte dô zehant
dâ er sînen herren vant.   2520
zuo dem sprach er alsus:
'herzoge Grêgôrjus,
ob ir iemer mîne vrouwen
lebende welt beschouwen,
so gesehet si vil drâte
oder ir komet ze spâte.

ich lie si in grôzer ungehabe.'
nû wart Grêgôrjus dar abe
vil harte riuwic und unvrô.
er sprach: 'geselle, wie redestû sô?   2530
jâ liez ich si an dirre stunt
vil harte vrô und wol gesunt.'
'herre, des wil ouch ich jehen.
jâ istz an dirre stunt geschehen.'

Ze walde wart niht mê gebiten:
vil balde si ze hûse riten.
da enwart (des wil ich iu verphlegen)
niht vil erbeizet under wegen
unz er vol hin kam
dâ sîn vreude ein ende nam,   2540
wande er muose schouwen
an sîner lieben vrouwen
ein swære ougenweide.
ir hiufeln was vor leide
diu rôsenvarwe entwichen,
diu schœne garwe erblichen:
sus vant er si tôtvar.
des entweich ouch im sîn vreude gar.
vil grôz jâmer dâ ergie:
wande zwei gelieber nie   2550
mannes ouge gesach.
der guote sündære sprach:

To live until the truth I learn
From him." To speed her lord's return,
She summoned him by messenger,
To leave the woods and haste to her.
    Departing then without delay
The messenger sped on his way,   2520
And finding his liege lord, spoke thus:
"Gracious Duke Gregorius,
If you ever want to see
My lady still alive, heed me,
And go to her; nor should you wait,
Or else you'll surely come too late.
I left her in great misery."
Gregorius heard this anxiously,
And, sore afflicted, said, "My lad,
What's this you say? Why is she sad?   2530
This very hour when I departed
She was well and cheerful-hearted."
"That's true, my lord, I will avow;
This change took place only just now."
    At once they left the woods for home.
Nor did they let their horses roam;
Nor did they even once dismount
(You may put faith in my account),
Until his journey's end; and there
His joy was destined to despair;   2540
For he was fated now to see
His dearest lady piteously
Present a melancholy sight.
Her rosiness had ebbed, and white
For sorrow were her cheeks, so wan,
And all her beauty faded, gone.
As he beheld her deathlike hue,
All happiness fled from him, too.
    Then great affliction came to pass—
A more devoted pair, alas,   2550
Never by mortal eye was seen.
"Lady, tell me, what does this mean?"

'vrouwe, wie gehabet ir iuch sô ?'
vil kûme gantwurte sị im dô,
wandẹ ir der sûft die sprâche brach.
mit halben worten si sprach:
'herrẹ, ich mac wol riuwic sîn.'
'waz wirret iu, liebiu vrouwe mîn ?'
'herre, des ist alsô vil
daz ichz gote klagen wil   2560
daz ich ie zer werlde kam:
wan mir ist diu Sælde gram.
vervluochet was diu stunde
von unsers herren munde,
dâ ich inne wart geborn.
Unsælde hât ûf mich gesworn
und behaltet vastẹ an mir den eit,
wan mir ie tûsent herzenleit
wider ein liep sint geschehen.
herrẹ, ir sult mir des verjehen   2570
von wannen ir geboren sît.
ez wære ê gewesen zît
der vrâge die ich nû begân:
ich wænẹ ich si verspætet hân.'
'vrouwẹ, ich weiz wol waz ir klaget:
iu hât etewer gesaget
daz ich sî ein ungeboren man.
weste ich wer iuch dar an
alsus geleidet hæte,
ez engelægen mîne ræte   2580
niemer unz ûf sînen tôt:
nû hel sich wol, des ist im nôt.
swer er ist, er hât gelogen:
ich bin von einem herzogen
vil endelichen geborn.
ir sult mir volgen âne zorn
daz wir der rede hie gedagen:
ich enmac iu vürbaz niht gesagen.'
    Sus antwurtẹ im diu vrouwe dô:
'der rede enist niht, herrẹ, alsô.   2590

The blameless sinner to her cried.
With difficulty she replied,
For sobs would cause her voice to choke,
And so in broken words she spoke,
"Lord, I have reason now to pine."
"What troubles you, dear lady mine?"
"So much disturbs me, lord, that I
Now must complain to God on high   2560
That ever I was born. I see
Unlucky is my destiny.
Accursed by our own dear Lord,
Truly, was that hour abhorred
When first I saw the light of day.
Misfortune swore to hold strong sway
Over me, and she has kept
Her oath against me; for I've wept
And suffered thousand miseries
For every joy. Lord, tell me, please,   2570
About your birth: whose child are you?
I should have asked you this, it's true,
Much sooner, when you first came here;
Too long I've put it off, I fear."
      "My lady, well I know what led
You so to grieve; someone has said
That I was born no nobleman.*
If I but knew who thus began
To cause your sorrow and lament,
Never once would I relent   2580
From pursuit until he died.
He'd better, for his own sake, hide!
He lied, whoever he may be,
Because I am assuredly
Of ducal parentage. I pray,
Do not grow angry, but obey,
And from discussion here refrain:
No further can I now explain."
      Then did the lady thus reply:
"Your words the state of things belie.   2590

jâ ensæhe ich den man
weizgot niemer lachendę an,
der mir von iu sagete
daz iu niht behagete:
er envunde hie niht guot antwurt.
jâ vürhtę ich, iuwer geburt
diu sî mir alze genôzsam.'
die tavel si her vür nam,
si sprach: 'sît ir der man
(dâ enhelt mich niht an)   2600
von dem hie an geschriben stât,
sô hât uns des tiuvels rât
versenket sêle unde lîp:
ich bin iuwer muoter und iuwer wîp.'

   Nû sprechet wie dâ wære
dem guoten sündære.
er was in leides gebote.
sînen zorn huop er hin ze gote,
er sprach: 'diz ist des ich ie bat,
daz mich got bræhte ûf die stat   2610
daz mir sô wol geschæhe
daz ich mit vreuden sæhe
mîne liebe muoter.
rîcher got vil guoter,
des hâstû anders mich gewert
dannę íchs an dich hân gegert.
ich gertes in mînem muote
nâch liebe und nâch guote:
nû hân ich si gesehen sô
daz ich des niemer wirde vrô,   2620
wandę ich si baz verbære
dannę ich ir sus heimlich wære.'
   Ich weiz wol daz Jûdas
niht riuwiger was
dô er sich vor leide hie

My lord, God knows that I would never
Look favorably on him who'd ever
Say anything to me I knew
Of distaste or offense to you.
He'd find no good response in me.
Indeed, your birth and ancestry
Are all too close to mine, I dread."
She brought the tablet forth and said,
"Are you the man (and do not lie
To me) to whom those words apply   2600
That stand in writing here? If so,
The Devil's plan has plunged us low,
Destroyed our souls and mortal life:
I am your mother and your wife!"

> Gregorius and his mother determine to do penance.

Can you imagine that young knight
And picture our good sinner's plight?
Beside himself, through sorrow dazed,
His angry voice to God he raised.
"Always have I prayed," he said,
"That God my wandering bestead   2610
And lead me to that very place
Where through good fortune I'd embrace
My mother happily at last.
O Gracious Lord, in power vast,
My wish now Thou hast granted me
So otherwise than wished of Thee.
For in my heart's deepest recess
I longed for love and happiness.
Now I have seen her in such way
That I shall ever rue the day.   2620
Would that on her I'd never set eyes
Than that I know her in this wise!"
When Judas hanged himself for grief,
Assuredly, it's my belief,
He no greater torment knew

danne ouch den zwein nû hie.
ouch entrûrte Dâvît
nihtes mêre zuo der zît
dô im kâmen mære
daz erslagen wære   2630
Saul unde Jônathas
und Absalôn der dâ was
sîn sun, der schœniste man
den wîp ze sun ie gewan.
  Swer ir jâmer und ir klagen
vol an ein ende solde sagen,
der müese wîser sîn dannę ich.
ich wænę ez wærę unmügelich
dazz iu mit einem munde
iemen vol gahten kunde.   2640
sich möhte vil nâch der tôt
gemâzet haben ze dirre nôt:
den hæten si, wærę er in komen,
ze voller wirtschaft genomen.
in wâren diu beide
gesament in glîchem leide,
beidiu sêle unde lîp.
wâ vriesch ie man oder wip
deheiner slahte swære
diu alsô garwe wære   2650
âne aller hande trôst?
diu sêlę entsaz den hellerôst:
sô was der lîp in beiden
bekumbert umbę ir scheiden.
ez hât geschaffet diu gotes kraft
ein missemüete geselleschaft
diu doch samet belîbe
under sêlę und under lîbe.
wan swaz dem lîbe sanfte tuot,
daz enist der sêle dehein guot: 2660
swâ mitę aber diu sêle ist genesen,
daz muoz des lîbes kumber wesen.
nû liten sį beidenthalben nôt:

Than the sorrow of these two.
Nor did David, Israel's King,
Mourn with deeper suffering
When tidings reached him that the twain,
Jonathan and Saul, were slain,   2630
As well as Absalom, his son,
His well beloved, his cherished one,
Whose beauty was beyond compare:
None handsomer did woman bear.
   He who wholly would convey
Their sad lamenting and dismay,
A wiser man than I must be.
It seems impossible to me
That any one man could relate
Fully of their tragic state.   2640
Such dire distress and misery
Are like to death's own agony.
If Death had come to them in threat,
A lavish welcome he'd have met.
Both like suffering were dealt
That both in soul and body felt.
Where is the woman or the man
Who, from the time the world began,
Has ever heard of any kind
Of sorrow for which one could find   2650
No manner of solace or of cheer?
Their souls Hell's fiery grate did fear;
Their bodies felt the torturing smart
And torment that they needs must part.
Although God made body and soul
To be one harmonious whole,*
Discordant is that unity:
Man's flesh and soul do not agree.
From what the flesh takes pleasure in
The soul of man no good can win,   2660
But that which brings the soul relief
Will mortify the flesh with grief.
With soul and body both in pain,

daz was ein zwivaltiger tôt.
  Diu vrouwę ûz grôzem jâmer sprach,
wan si den jâmer ane sach:
'ouwê ich vervluochtez wîp!
jâ kumbert maniger den lîp,
daz des diu sêle werde vrô:
dem geschiht ouch alsô.   2670
so bewiget sich manic man und wîp
der sêle umbe den lîp
und lebet in dirre werlde wol.
nû enmac ich noch ensol
mînem lîbe niht des gejehen
des im ze guote sî geschehen:
ist mir diu sêle noch verlorn,
sô ist der heize gotes zorn
vil gar ûf mich gevallen
als den vervluochten allen.   2680
mich wundert, nâch der missetât
die mir der lîp begangen hât,
daz mich diu erde geruochet tragen.
sun herre, muget ir mir sagen
(wan ir habet der buoche vil gelesen),
möhte aber dehein buoze wesen
über sus schämlich missetât,
ob des nû ist dehein rât
(dez ich wol muoz getrûwen)
ich enmüeze die helle bûwen,   2690
dâ mite ich doch verschulde daz
daz si mir doch etewaz
senfter danne maniges leben
der ouch der helle ist gegeben?'
  'Muoter', sprach Grêgôrjus,
'gesprechet niemer mêrę alsus:
ez ist wider dem gebote.
niht verzwîvelt an gote:
ir sult vil harte wol genesen.
jâ hân ich einen trôst gelesen   2700
daz got die wâren riuwe hât

They suffered now a twofold bane.
  The lady faced their misery
And from its very depths cried she,
"Oh, woe is me! Accursed am I!
Many a one does mortify
His body to rejoice his soul,
And he attains his longed-for goal.   2670
Many a man or woman elects
To serve the body and neglects
His soul that he on earth may lead
A life of ease. Now I, indeed,
Can not, nor should I, benefit
My body or concede to it.
If my soul, too, is lost to me,
God's flaming wrath* has utterly
Descended now on me as well
As on all sinners damned to Hell.   2680
It is a marvel to me how
The earth deigns to support me now,
After my body's sins, so great.
My son and lord,* can you relate
(Since you've read many books) to me,
If there perhaps some penance be
For such a shameful, heinous deed—
For which I know that I shall need
To suffer in Hell's Pit (as I
Must now full well believe)—whereby   2690
I may merit that Hell be
A little easier for me
Than for so many who must dwell
Likewise condemned in burning Hell?"
  "Mother," spoke Gregorius,
"Do not ever again speak thus;
It is against the Law; forbear,
And never of the Lord despair.
You will most surely find salvation.
Yes, I've read of one consolation: 2700
Repentance that is genuine

ze buozę über alle missetât.
iuwer sêlę ist nie sô ungesunt,
wirt iu daz ouge zeiner stunt
von herzelîcher riuwe naz,
ir sît genesen, geloubet daz.
belîbet bî iuwerm lande.
an spîsę und an gewande
sult ir dem lîbę entziehen,
gemach und vreude vliehen.   2710
ir ensultz sô niht behalten
daz irs iht wellet walten
durch dehein werltlich êre,
niuwan daz ir deste mêre
gote rihtet mit dem guote.
jâ tuot ez wirs dem muote,
der guotes lebens wal hât
und er sich sîn âne begât,
danne ob es enbirt ein man
des er teil nie gewan.   2720
ir sît ein schuldic wîp:
des lât engelten den lîp
mit tägelîcher arbeit
sô daz im sî widerseit
des er dâ aller meiste ger.
sus habet in unz er iu wer
in der riuwen bande.
den gelt von iuwerm lande
den teilet mit den armen:
sô müezet ir gotę erbarmen.   2730
bestiftet iuwer eigen,
swâ iuwer wîsen zeigen,
mit rîchen klôstern (daz ist guot):
sus senftet sînen zornmuot
den wir sô gar erbelget hân.
ich wil im ouch ze buoze stân.
vrouwe, liebiu muoter mîn,
diz sol diu jungist rede sîn
die ich iemer wider iuch getuo.

God deems as penance for every sin.
No matter how sick your soul may grow,
Let tears but reach your eyes and flow
In true remorse, you will achieve
Salvation; this firmly believe.
Remaining here within your land,
Clothe yourself with sparing hand;
Be abstinent in food and drink;
Shun comfort, and from pleasure shrink.   2710
No possessions should you keep
For yourself with which to reap
Worldly fame of any kind
Save if by means of them you find
To God you're able to atone
The better. Electing to disown
The goods of life one does possess
Hurts more and causes more distress
Than to deprive oneself of what
One never in this world had got.   2720
You are a sinful woman; hence,
Let your body in penitence
Perform hard labor day by day,
So that it is in every way
Denied what it wants most of all.
Thus keep it in the shackling thrall
Of true remorse throughout your days.
All the money that you raise
From your realm, share with the poor.
God's mercy you may thus secure.   2730
Where'er your counselors designate
Establish on your own estate
Mighty convents (good are these).
The wrath of Him you'd thus appease
Whom we've so much provoked. I, too,
Penance unto Him will do.
My lady, and my mother dear,
These words that I say to you here
Shall be my last with you, alas.

wir suln ez bringen dar zuo   2740
daz uns noch got gelîche
gesamene in sînem rîche.
ich engesihe iuch niemer mê.
wir wæren baz gescheiden ê.
dem lande und dem guote
und werltlîchem muote
dem sî hiute widerseit.'
hin tet er diu rîchen kleit
und schiet sich von dem lande
mit dürftigen gewande.   2750

We may yet bring it to pass 2740
That our Lord, no longer loath,
In His realm will unite us both.
I'll not see you henceforth. Indeed,
Would we had sooner said, 'God speed.'
Now let my realm and my possessions,
Let the world and its professions
Be renounced this very day!"
His splendid robes he laid away,
And put on beggar's garb, and then
Departed from the land again. 2750

Ez wâren dem rîchen dürftigen
alle gnâde verzigen,
wan daz er al sîn arbeit
mit willigem muote leit.
er gertę in sînem muote
daz in got der guote
sandę in eine wüeste,
dâ er inne müeste
büezen unz an sînen tôt.
spilnde bestuont er dise nôt.   2760
er schûhte âne mâze
die liute und die strâze
undz blôze gevilde:
allez gegen der wilde
sô rihte der arme sîne wege.
er wuot diu wazzer bî dem stege.
mit marwen vüezen ungeschuoch
streich er walt unde bruoch
sô daz er sîns gebetes phlac
ungâz unz án den dritten tac.   2770
   Nû gie ein stîc (der was smal)
nâ bî einem sê ze tal.
den ergreif der lîplôse man
und gevolgetę im dan
unz er ein hiuselîn gesach:
dar kêrte der arme durch gemach.

CHAPTER IV

Gregorius' Seventeen Years of Atonement

Gregorius seeks shelter in a fisherman's hut.

Ease and comfort of every kind*
The wealthy beggar now declined.
He renounced all joys but one:
Gladness in the task* begun.
He felt great longing in his breast
That God, Most Gracious and Most Blest,
Direct him to a wilderness
Where he might stay, and comfortless
Do penance till he live no more.
Joyfully his trials he bore.   2760
The open field, the simple road,
The highway, men, and their abode,
He shied away from, as he traced
His every step towards trackless waste.
Skirting every bridge, he'd wade
Through the water's barricade.
With his tender feet unshod
He roamed the forests, and he trod
The marshes, ceasing not to fast
And pray, until three days had passed.   2770
    There was a path, a narrow way,
Along the sea, downhill it lay.
Gregorius now wearily
Pursued this path till he could see
A little hut. There in his quest
He halted for the sake of rest.

ein vischære hete gehûset dâ,
den dûhte daz niender anderswâ
daz vischen wæger wære.
den bat der riuwesære   2780
der herberge durch got.
von dem duldę er merren spot
dannę er gewon wære.
als im der vischære
sînen schœnen lîp gesach,
er wegetez houbet unde sprach:
'jâ dû starker trügenære!
ob ez sô wære
daz ich der tôrheit wielte
daz ich dich vrâz behielte,   2790
sô næme dich, grôz gebûre,
der rede vil untûre,
so ich hîntę entsliefe und mîn wîp,
daz dû uns beiden den lîp
næmest umbę unser guot.
ouwê wie übel diu werlt tuot,
daz die liute under in
duldent solhen ungewin,
sô manigen unnützen man
des got nie êre gewan,   2800
und wüestent doch die liute.
ez wærę ein breit geriute
ze dînen armen wol bewant:
ez zæme baz in dîner hant
ein houwe und ein gart
danne dîn umbevart.
ez ist ein wol gewantez brôt
(daz dir der tiuvel tuo den tôt!)
daz dû vrâz verswendest.
wie dû dîn sterke schendest!   2810
rûmez hûs vil drâte.'
     Nû was ez harte spâte.
do emphie der sündære
diz schelten âne swære

A fisherman had settled there
Whose thought had been that he nowhere
Could fish more advantageously.
To him the penitent made plea   2780
To give him shelter for God's sake.
The loud abuse he had to take
Surpassed what he had ever heard.
With scorn the fisherman demurred.
   Seeing the sinner's handsome frame,
He shook his head and cried, "For shame,
You big swindler! Ruffian! Fie!
Not the slightest doubt have I,
If I were fool enough to feed
A glutton like you, a rogue, indeed,   2790
You scamp, you scoundrel, much you'd care
What was said or what you'd swear.
While I and my wife slept tonight
You'd murder both of us, all right,
To rob us of our property.
How evil is this world, ah me!
That people among themselves allow
Such mischief to exist, and bow
To many such useless knaves, like you,
Who never honor God, and, too,   2800
Who plunder human beings. Now,
A good-sized field fit for the plow
Would suit quite well your sturdy arm;
And it would do you far less harm
To hold a hoe and switch in hand
Than rove as vagrant through the land.
Fine use, indeed, would have that bread
With which you, glutton, would be fed!
The Devil take you! How you put
Your strength to shame! Now take your foot   2810
From out my house, and leave straightway."
   Though it had grown late in the day,
Without complaint, without demur,
The sinner took the fisher's slur

und mit lachendem muote.
sus antwurtẹ im der guote:
'herrẹ, ir habet mir wâr geseit.
swer guote gewarheit
im selben schaffet, daz ist sin.'
guoter naht wunschtẹ er in 2820
und schiet lachende dan.
der vil wîselôse man
hôrte gerne disen spot
unde lobete sîn got,
der selben unwirdikeit.
swelh versmæcheit unde leit
sînem lîbe wære geschehen,
diu hetẹ er gerne gesehen.
hetẹ im der ungeborne
grôze slege von zorne 2830
über sînen rücke geslagen,
daz hetẹ er gerne vertragen,
ob sîner sünden swære
iht deste ringer wære.
  Des übelen vischæres wîp
erbarmte sich über sînen lîp.
si bedûhtes daz er wærẹ
niht ein trügenære.
des scheltens des in der man tete
umbe sîn dürfticlîche bete, 2840
des ervolleten ir diu ougen.
si sprach: 'des ist unlougen
diz ensî ein guot man:
zewârẹ ich sihe imz wol an.
got lâze dichs niht engelten:
dû hâst getân ein schelten
daz dînem heile nâhen gât.
dû weist wol daz dîn hûs stât
den liuten alsô verre.
swenne dich unser herre 2850
dîner sælden ermande
und dir sînen boten sande,

And scolding words with friendly mien,
And then replied, calm and serene:
"Sir, you have spoken truth to me.
Of course, a man acts sensibly
To safeguard his own life aright!"
He bade the fisherman good night   2820
And left him with a friendly smile.
The helpless man rejoiced the while
He heard the fisher's taunts and jeers
And praised his God for all the sneers
And ignominy he'd just felt.
No matter what he'd have been dealt
Of suffering, derision, pain,
He would have welcomed it as gain.
Had the fisher, lowly born,
Struck heavy blows in angry scorn   2830
Upon his back, without a cry
Would he have borne them, if thereby
The burden of his sins could be
The lighter in the least degree.

      The wicked fisher's wife began
To feel compassion for the man.
He seemed to her not to behave
Like a rogue or arrant knave.
Her eyes began to fill with tears
As her husband's scolding jeers   2840
Mocked the begging man in need.
She said, "You surely must concede
This is a good man. I know well
He is: just looking I can tell.
May God not make you pay for this:
Reviling him you've been remiss,
Endangering your soul's salvation.
Your house lies hid in this location,
Remote from people, you'll admit.
Should our Heavenly Lord see fit   2850
To warn you of redemption's need
And send His messenger,* indeed

den soldestû emphâhen baz
und vil wol bedenken daz:
dir enkam dehein dürftige nie,
sît wir begunden bûwen hie,
niuwan dirre armman
der ouch niht vil dar an gewan.
swelh man sich alle tage
begân muoz von bejage,   2860
als dû mit zwîvel hâst getân,
der solde got vor ougen hân:
daz tuo aber noch, daz râte ich dir.
sô helfe dir got und gunne mir
daz ich im ruofen müeze.
sîn vart diu ist unsüeze:
ja engât er nie sô balde,
er enbenahte in dem walde.
engezzent in die wolve niht,
daz aber vil lîhte geschiht,   2870
sô muoz er dâ ungâz ligen
und aller gnâden verzigen.
lâ mir daz ze gewalte
daz ich in hînte behalte.'
sus gesenfte si mit güete
dem vischære sîn gemüete,
daz er ir des gunde
daz si dâ zestunde
dem wîselôsen nâch lief
und daz si im her wider rief.   2880
Dô si in her wider gewan,
dô was dem vischenden man
sîn âbentezzen bereit.
der grôzen unwirdikeit
die er âne aller slahte nôt
dem edeln dürftigen bôt,
der wolde inz wîp ergetzen
und begunde im vür setzen
ir aller besten spîse.
die versprach der wîse,   2890

You should receive Him with more grace,
Considering carefully our case:
Never since we first began
To live here has a needy man
Come to our door, save this one here,
And he did not gain much, that's clear.
Who in uncertainty each day
Must fish in order to allay   2860
His hunger, and does so, like you,
Should always keep the Lord in view.
I counsel you to do that still,
So help you God! And grant my will
And let me summon him back here.
His journey is so bitter drear.
Within the woods by close of day
He will be caught, haste as he may.
Wolves with ease could overpower him,
And if they did not devour him   2870
He'd still lie hungry all the night,
Deprived of comfort in his plight.
Allow me then to have my way
That this night he with us may stay."
    With gentleness she mollified
The fisherman, and so did guide
His spirit that he acquiesced
Without ado to her request:
She was allowed to hasten then
And call the wanderer back again.   2880
    When back she brought him with halloo,
The fisher's evening meal was due,
And she prepared it with all speed.
Now since the fisher had indeed
In anger raged and with taunts shamed
The noble beggar, and had blamed
The man quite without cause, she wished
To make amends to him, and dished
For him the choicest food she had.
No matter how she urged and bade   2890

swie vil si in genôte.
ein ranft von haberbrôte
wart im dar gewunnen
und ein trunc eins brunnen.
alsô sprach er wider daz wîp
daz kûme sîn sündic lîp
der spîse wert wære.

 Dô in der vischære
die kranken spîse ezzen sach,
dô schalt er in aber unde sprach: 2900
'ouwê daz ich diz sehen sol!
ja erkenne ich trügenære wol
und alle trügewîse.
du enhâst sô kranker spîse
dich niht unz her begangen.
ez enschînet an dînen wangen
weder durst noch hungers nôt:
diu sint sô veiz und sô rôt.
ez engesach nie man noch wîp
deheinen wætlîchern lîp: 2910
den hâstû niht gewunnen
von brôte noch von brunnen.
dû bist gemestet harte wol,
dîn schenkel sleht, dîn vüeze hol,
dîn zêhen gelîmet unde lanc,
dîn nagel lûter unde blanc.
dîn vüeze solden unden
breit sîn und zeschrunden
als einem wallenden man.
nu enkiuse ich dînen schenkeln an   2920
deheinen val noch stôz:
si ensint niht lange gewesen blôz.
wie wol si des bewart sint
daz si vrost oder wint
iender habe gerüeret!
sleht und unzevüeret
ist dîn hâr und dîn lîch
eim gemasten vrâze gelîch.

Him eat, the prudent man declined.
Water from a well, a rind
Of oaten bread he did at last
Accept, and after his repast
He thus the fisher's wife addressed:
His sinful body, he confessed,
Was scarcely worthy of the food.
   As the fisherman now viewed
Him at his slender fare, once more
Railing at him as before,   2900
"That I should see this with my eyes!"
He said, "How well I recognize
A cheat and every kind of cheating!
You certainly have not been eating
Up till now so meagerly.
On your cheeks I do not see
The pinch of cold or hunger's sign:
So fat they are; so pink they shine.
No one has ever seen by far
So handsome a man as you are.   2910
That body of yours has not been fed
With simple water and simple bread.
You have a well-filled-out physique;
You have high arches; your thighs are sleek;
Your toes are long and lie quite tight*
Together, with clean nails shining white.
Your feet should be both flat and broad,
If you're a pilgrim and no fraud;
And chapped and calloused should they be.
Now on your thighs I do not see   2920
The signs of any blow or fall;
They have been bare not long at all.
How well indeed have they been shielded
That their skin has never yielded
To touch of bitter frost or wind.
Your hair lies smooth and disciplined.
From your appearance, easily,
A fattened glutton you could be.

dîn arme und dîn hende
stânt âne missewende: 2930
die sint sô sleht und sô wîz:
dû hâst ir anderen vlîz
an dîner heimlîche
dan dû hie tuost gelîche.
ich bin des âne sorgen
du enbeginnest dich morgen
dirre nôt ergetzen.
dû kanst dich baz gesetzen,
dâ dûz veile vindest,
dâ dû wol überwindest   2940
weizgot alle dîne nôt,
dâ diz dürre haberbrôt
und dirre brunne wære
dînem munde unmære.'
    Dise rede emphie der guote
mit lachendem muote
und woldes geniezen wider got
daz er leit sô grôzen spot
von alsô swacher geburt.
er engap im dehein antwurt   2950
unz ûf die stunde
daz er in begunde
vrâgen der mære
waz mannes er wære.
er sprach: 'herre, ich bin ein man
daz ich niht ahte wizzen kan
mîner süntlîchen schulde
und suoche um gotes hulde
ein stat in dirre wüeste,
uf der ich iemer müeste   2960
büezen unz an mînen tôt
vaste mit des lîbes nôt.
ez ist hiute der dritte tac
daz ich der werlde verphlac
und allez nâch der wilde gie.
ich enversach mich niht hie

Your hands and arms, both left and right,
Are all so smooth and soft and white: 2930
There's no flaw on them anywhere.
How very different is the care
You've given them in secrecy
From what you now pretend to me.
Tomorrow you will compensate,
I have no doubt, for the hard fate
You've had to suffer here today.
You'll find a better place to stay
Where you will pay, and where, God knows,
From all your hardships, I suppose,   2940
You'll soon recover, and where, instead,
Such dry, simple oaten bread
And plain water from this spring
A bad taste to your mouth would bring."
    The good man cheerfully had borne
The lowly man's harsh words and scorn,
And wished that he would merit gain
In God's eyes for the great disdain
Endured from man of birth so mean.
With no words did he intervene   2950
Until the fisherman at last
Began to ask him of his past
And to inquire pointedly
Who he was in verity.
    He said, "I am a man, good sir,
Who is not able to aver
How far his sinful guilt extends;
To gain God's grace and make amends,
Within this dreary waste, so bare,
I seek a spot secluded where   2960
I may do penance till I die,
And there my body mortify.
Three suns have risen since the day
When from the world I turned away
To wander in this wilderness
On and on. How could I guess

gebiuwes noch liute.
sît daz mich hiute
mîn wec zuo iu getragen hât,
sô suoche ich gnâde unde rât.   2970
wizzet ir iender hie bî
ein stat diu mir gevellic sî,
einen wilden stein oder ein hol,
des bewîset mich: sô tuot ir wol.'

Des antwurte im der vischære dô:
'sît dû des gerst, vriunt, sô wis vrô.
dêswâr ich bringe dich wol hein.
ich weiz hie bî uns einen stein,
ein lützel über disen sê:
dâ mac dir wol werden wê.   2980
swie wir daz erringen
daz wir dich dar bringen,
dâ mahtû dich mit swæren tagen
dînes kumbers wol beklagen.
er ist dir gnuoc wilde.
wart des ie dehein bilde
daz dîn muot ze riuwe stât,
sô tuon ich dir einen ganzen rât.
ich hân ein îsenhalten
nû lange her behalten: 2990
die wil ich dir ze stiure geben,
daz dû bestætest dîn leben
ûf dem selben steine.
die sliuz ze dînem beine.
geriuwet dich danne der wanc,
sô muostû under dînen danc
doch dar ûfe bestân.
ez ist der stein alsô getân,
swer joch ledige vüeze hât,

I'd meet with man or dwelling here!
And since my path, it would appear,
This day has led me on to you,
Your grace I ask, and counsel, too.   2970
If you know of a place, nearby,
A desolate cliff, or cave, that I
Might fitly choose, then show me it:
So doing, you do benefit."

The fisherman takes Gregorius to a desolate
island cliff and locks him in fetters. Gregorius
remains alone on the island for seventeen years.

In answer came the fisher's voice,
"If that is all you want, rejoice.
I'll take you where you wish to go.
Near us, the very spot I know,
A rock, a short way out to sea—
There you can suffer, friend, trust me!   2980
Once we succeed in getting you
Out on the rock, without ado
You can lament your sinful ways
Within the course of wretched days.
It's desolate enough for you
Out there. If what you've said is true—
That on repentance you are bent—
I'll counsel you to full extent.
  "I've had in my possession here
An iron shackle many a year.   2990
Here, take it as a gift from me
To help you dwell here steadfastly,
Secure upon that very rock;
Your leg within this fetter lock:
If doubt besets and troubles you,
The only thing you then can do,
Willy-nilly, will be to stay.
The cliff's so steep as to dismay
Even him whose feet are free:

daz er unsanfte drabe gât.   3000
sî dir nû ernest dar zuo,
sô ganc slâfen und wis vruo,
dîn îsenhalten nim ze dir,
sitze an mîn schef ze mir,
sô ich vor tage vischen var.
ich kêre durch dîn liebe dar
und hilfe dir ûf den stein
und behefte dir dîniu bein
mit der îsenhalten,
daz dû dâ muost alten   3010
und daz dû wærlîche
ûf disem ertrîche
mich niemer gedrangest.
des bin ich gar âne angest.'
swie erz mit hônschaft tæte,
sô wâren diz die ræte
rehte als er wünschen wolde,
ob er wünschen solde.
    Nû was der unguote man
harte strenge dar an   3020
daz er im deheines gemaches
sô vil sôs obedaches
in sînem hûse engunde.
sîn wîp im enkunde
mit allen ir sinnen
daz niht an gewinnen
daz er dar inne wære beliben.
er wart en hundes wîs getriben
an den hof vür die tür.
dâ gie er vrœlichen vür.   3030
    Des nahtes wart er geleit
wider sîner gewonheit
in ein sô armez hiuselîn
daz ez niht armer enmöhte sîn:
daz was zevallen, âne dach.
man schuof dem vürsten solch gemach
der vil gar unmære

No one can climb down easily.   3000
If you're telling me no lies,
Early to bed, and early rise!
Your iron shackle with you take.
Get in my boat before daybreak
With me, when I row out to fish.
I'll head, to gratify your wish,
Toward the cliff; and up the rock
I'll help you, and your legs I'll lock
Within the iron fetter fast,
So that as long as you will last   3010
You'll have to stay right there, and then
Upon this earth you'll never again
Be any trouble at all to me:
Of that I'm sure as sure can be."
    Though jeeringly the fisher taunted,
Just this Gregorius had wanted.
If he'd been wishing for advice,
This he'd have wished for in a trice.
And now the fisher proved to be
Cruel and harsh to such degree,   3020
All comfort he begrudged him there
And would not even shelter spare
Within the house beneath his roof.
Despite all effort and reproof,
His wife could not make him relent,
Nor could she bring him to consent
To have Gregorius there abide.
Driven like a dog outside,
Chased from the door, he went, serene,
Forth to the yard with cheerful mien.   3030
    That night he couched so wretchedly,
To former wont quite contrary—
So wretched was his shelter there,
More wretched can be found nowhere:
Tumbledown and roofless—such
The lodging for this lord—a hutch
That would be repugnant quite

sînem aschman wære.
er vant dar inne swachen rât,
weder strô noch bettewât: 3040
im truoc daz guot wîp dar in
ein lützel rôres under in.
dô leite er gehalten
sîne îsenhalten
und sîne tavele dar zuo,
daz er si vunde morgen vruo.
   Wie lützel er die naht gelac!
sîns gebetes er phlac
unz in diu müede übergie.
dô er ze slâfe gevie,   3050
dô was ez nâhen bî dem tage.
dô vuor der vischære nâch bejage:
dar zuo was er vruo bereit
nâch sîner gewonheit.
nû ruofte er sînem gaste:
dô slief er alsô vaste,
als ez von grôzer müede kam,
daz er sîn rüefen niht vernam.
dô ruofte er im anderstunt,
er sprach: 'mir was ê wol kunt   3060
daz disem trügenære
der rede niht ernest wære.
ich engerüefe dir niemer mê.'
alsus gâhte er zuo dem sê.
   Dô diz daz guote wîp ersach,
si wahte in ûf unde sprach:
'wiltû varen, guot man,
sich, dâ sûmestû dich an.
mîn wirt wil varen ûf den sê.'
dô enwart niht gebiten mê.   3070
er vorhte im grôzer swære,
daz er versûmet wære:
dâ wider wart er aber dô
sînes muotes harte vrô,
daz er in solde vüeren hin

To his lowest serving-wight.
Scant were the furnishings in there:
Of straw or bedding it was bare.   3040
The wife, good soul, dragged out anon
Rushes for him to lie upon.
Therein he stored his iron fetter
With his tablet, that the better
He might find them straight away
Early on the following day.
   How brief the time he lay abed!*
He spent the hours at prayer instead,
Till weariness came over him,
And sleep possessed his every limb   3050
Just as the day to dawn began.
This was the hour the fisherman
Used to get ready with dispatch
To row out early for his catch.
He called aloud now to his guest
Who did not hear himself addressed:
He lay in heavy slumber's keep
And slept exhaustion's weary sleep.
The fisher called to him once more
And said, "How well I knew before,   3060
That swindler didn't mean a word
He said in earnest—I've not erred.
You won't be called again by me!"
He hurried off then toward the sea.
   The good wife, seeing this, then woke
Gregorius, and thus she spoke:
"My good man, if you want to go,
You're late now; do not linger so.
My husband's setting out to sea."
The sleeper rose immediately.   3070
He feared—and suffered on this score—
That he too late would reach the shore.
Yet at the same time, nevertheless,
His heart was full of happiness
That he would now be shown the way,

als er gelobete wider in.
diu liebe und diu leide
die macheten im beide
ze sînem gâhenne daz
daz er der tavele vergaz   3080
die er zallen zîten
truoc bî sîner sîten.
die îsenhalten truoc er dan
unde gâhte nâch dem man.
    Er ruofte durch got daz er sîn bite.
alsus vuorte er in mit unsite
ûf jenen wilden stein:
dâ beslôz er im diu bein
vaste in die îsenhalten.
er sprach: 'hie muostû alten.   3090
dich envüere mit sînen sinnen
der tiuvel von hinnen,
dû enkumest hin abe niemer mê.'
den slüzzel warf er in den sê.
er sprach: 'daz weiz ich âne wân,
swenne ich den slüzzel vunden hân
ûz der tiefen ünde,
sô bistû âne sünde
und wol ein heiliger man.'
er lie in dâ und schiet er dan.   3100
    Der arme Grêgôrjus,
nû beleip er alsus
ûf dem wilden steine
aller gnâden eine.
er enhete anderen gemach,
niuwan der himel was sîn dach.
er enhete deheinen scherm mê
vür rîfen noch vür snê,
vür wint noch vür regen
niuwan den gotes segen.   3110
im wâren kleider vremede,
niuwan ein hærîn hemede:
im wâren bein und arme blôz.

As he'd been promised yesterday.
Joy and grief within his breast
In conflict made him so distressed
That they, together with his haste,
Made him forget, as off he raced,   3080
The tablet he was wont to bear
On his person everywhere.
He took the iron gyve and ran
In haste after the fisherman.
   He called to him by heaven to wait.
The fisher, then, with boorish prate,
Rowed him to the desolate rock.
In iron gyves, with key and lock,
His legs he shackled fast and said,
"Here you can grow old till you're dead!   3090
Unless the Devil with his guile
Removes you from this rocky isle,
From here you'll get down never more!"
Into the sea, far from the shore,
He cast away the key, and then,
"If ever I find this key again
From out the deep, assuredly
I'll know," he said, "that you are free
Of sin, a holy man instead."
He left him there, and off he sped.   3100
   Unfortunate Gregorius
On that desolate cliff was thus
In utter solitude now left,
Of every comfort quite bereft.
The only chamber where he could lie
Had as its roof the heavenly sky.
He had no shield that would avail
Against the snow, the rain, the hail;
The gusts of wind blew in his face;
His sole protection was God's grace.   3110
Upon his body he wore naught
Except a hair shirt that was wrought
To leave his arms and legs quite bare.

er enmöhte der spîse die er nôz,
als ich iu rehte nû sage,
weizgot vierzehen tage
vor dem hunger niht geleben,
im enwære gegeben
der trôstgeist von Kriste
der im daz leben vriste, 3120
daz er vor hunger genas.
ich sagę iu waz sîn spîse was.
ez seic ûz dem steine
wazzers harte kleine.
dar under gruop er ein hol:
daz wart mit einem trunke vol.
ez was sô kleine dazz nâch sage
zwischen naht unde tage
vil kûme vollez geran.
daz tranc der gnâdenlôse man. 3130
sus lebetę er sibenzehen jâr.
daz dunket manigen niht wâr:
des gelouben velsche ich.
wan gotę ist niht unmügelich
ze tuonne swaz er wil:
im ist deheines wunders ze vil.

He would have died of lack of fare—
The truth I tell you now—God knows,
He'd have succumbed to hunger's throes
In fourteen days at very most,
Had Christ not sent the Holy Ghost,
The Paraclete,* his life to stay
And to sustain him; in that way   3120
Was he healed of hunger there.
I'll tell you what he had as fare.

From out that desolate stone abode,
Drop by drop, some water flowed.
He dug a hole beneath the drip
Where it filled for a single sip.
So slow the trickle was, so slight,
The story goes, that 'twixt the night
And day, the hole was scarcely filled.
His thirst the hapless man here stilled.   3130

Thus he spent seven years and ten.
"That is not true," think many men.
False the faith* of such a one!
For God His Will has ever done:
All's possible within His sight,
No miracle's beyond His might.

Dô der gnâden eine
ûf dem wilden steine
sibenzehen jâr gesaz
unde got an im vergaz   3140
sîner houbetschulde
unz ûf sîne hulde,
dô starp, als ich ez las,
der dô ze Rôme bâbest was.
alse schiere dô er starp,
ein ieglich Rômære warp
besunder sînem künne
durch des guotes wünne
umbe den selben gewalt.
ir strît wart sô manicvalt   3150
daz si beide durch nît
unde durch der êren gît
bescheiden niene kunden
wem si des stuoles gunden.
   Nû rieten si über al
daz si liezen die wal
an unseren herren got,
daz sîn genâde und sîn gebot
erzeicte wer in wære
guot ze rihtære.   3160

CHAPTER V

Gregorius Becomes Pope

Upon the death of the pope at Rome, two noble
Romans have a miraculous dream concerning
the pope's successor. They ride off in search of
the holy man revealed in their dream.

Now when upon that desolate stone
This hapless man had lived alone
For seventeen years, and when the Lord
Forgot his deadly sin abhorred,   3140
But ever to His glory shed
His grace upon the sinner's head,
He who was pope at Rome then died.
Thus books to me have testified.
Scarcely was he laid to rest
When every Roman tried his best,
Each for his kinsman to attain
The papal power and domain
For sake of profit in this life.
So widespread became their strife   3150
That in their jealousy and greed
For honors, they could not concede
The choice to any that they judged;
To each the throne they all begrudged.
    Then one and all reached this accord:
To let the choice rest with our Lord,
Whose will would show and let them know,
By the grace He would bestow,
Who He thought would be best fit
Upon the papal throne to sit.   3160

dienstes si im gedâhten
daz si ouch volbrâhten
mit almuosen und mit gebete.
got dô genædeclichen tete
der ie der guoten vrâge riet.
eines nahtes er beschiet
wîsen Rômæren zwein,
an den volleclichen schein
diu triuwe und diu wârheit
daz ir wort was ein eit.   3170
    Dâ si besunder lâgen
und ir gebetes phlâgen,
diu gotes stimme sprach in zuo
daz si des næhsten tages vruo
Rômære zesamene bæten
und in daz kunt tæten
waz gotes wille wære
umbe ir rihtære.
ez wære gesezzen eine
ûf einem wilden steine   3180
ein man in Equitânjâ
(den enweste nieman dâ)
vol sibenzehen jâr:
ze dem wære vür wâr
der stuol vil wol bewant
und wære Grêgôrjus genant.
daz erz in beiden tete kunt,
daz meinde daz eines mannes munt
niht enmac erziugen wol
swaz grôze kraft haben sol.   3190
    Nu enweste ir deweder niht
umbe dise geschiht
daz in diu rede beiden
des nahtes wart bescheiden,
unz si zesamene kâmen
undz under in vernâmen.
und als si getâten
als si vernomen hâten,

In holy service to the Lord
They worshipped Him, and Him adored,
With almsgiving and prayer combined;
And God was graciously inclined,
Who always heeds the righteous' plea.
He manifested His decree
To two wise Roman men, one night;
Both glowed so radiant, alight
With truth and virtue, that their word
Was as an oath to all who heard.   3170
    As each was in his home and there,
Engaged in customary prayer,
The voice of God spoke to the two
And told them while the day was new
To bid the Romans congregate
And hearken to what they'd relate,
For they would then God's choice make known
Of who as pope should mount the throne.
It was their duty to explain
That in the land of Aquitaine   3180
There had been living all alone
(To no one was this matter known),
On a wild cliff, remote from men,
Fully seven years and ten,
One suited for the Holy See,
A man whose name was Gregory.
God revealed this to them both,
For He knew that men are loath
In one man's witnessing to see
What should have great authority.   3190
    Now at the time neither one knew
That this had happened to the two:
That to both this had occurred—
That each that night the message heard;
Not till they met with one another
Did they learn it, each from the other.
In accordance with God's say
They bore themselves, and from the way

dô einer sîne rede gesprach
und der ander mite jach, 3200
do geloubeten Rômære
vil gerne disiu mære:
ze gote wâren si vil vrô.
die alten herren wurden dô
ze boten beide gesant
in Equitânjam daz lant,
daz si den guoten man
suochten und in bræhten dan.

Nû bekumberte si daz:
der stein dâ er ûfe saz 3210
der enwart in niht benant.
mit zwîvel vuoren si in daz lant.
dâ gevorscheten si gnuoc,
swar si ir wec truoc:
nu enkunde in nieman gesagen.
daz begunden si von herzen klagen
dem der in beruochet
der gnâde an in suochet.
nu gesande in got in ir sin.,
solden si iemer vinden in, 3220
daz man in danne müeste
suochen in der wüeste.
sus begunden si gâhen,
dâ siz gebirge sâhen,
in die wilde zuo dem sê.
der zwîvel tet in harte wê
daz si niht wizzen kunden
wâ si in vunden.

Dô wîste si diu wilde
ze walde von gevilde. 3230
sus vuor diu wegelôse diet,
als in ir gemüete riet,
irre unz an den dritten tac.
einen stîc âne huofslac
den ergriffen si dô:
des wurden si vil harte vrô.

Each spoke and was corroborated
By the other in what he stated,   3200
The Romans willingly believed
The tidings they had thus received,
And unto God were joyous then.
Dispatched were both old noblemen
As messengers to Aquitaine
To seek throughout the whole domain
And find the holy man, and then
With him return to Rome again.

    Now one thing troubled both: the stone,
On which Gregorius sat alone,   3210
Had not been given any name.
Hence with uncertainty they came
To Aquitaine, where, diligent,
They searched on every road they went.
No one could give them information.
This they deplored with lamentation
To Him Whose mercy ever reaches
Whoever Him for grace beseeches.
Now God put this thought in their mind:
If whom they sought they were to find,   3220
Their search had to be undertaken
In desolate wastes, by men forsaken.
They started with celerity
Toward the mountains they could see,
And went on through the wilderness
Close by the sea. They felt distress
In being at a loss to know
How now to find him—where to go.

    The wilderness then led them on
From open fields to woods anon.   3230
Without direction thus they sped;
Alone by feeling were they led,
And wandered, lost, till the third day.
A narrow footpath on their way,
Where horse's hoof had never gone,
To their good fortune they entered on.

der grasige wec ungebert
der truoc si verrẹ in einen wert,
dâ der vischære bî dem sê
saz, dâ von ich iu sagetẹ ê,   3240
der den sælderîchen
sô ungezogenlîchen
in sînen dürften emphie
und die übelẹ an im begie
daz er in durch sînen haz
sazte, dâ er noch saz,
ûf den dürren wilden stein
und im dâ sîniu bein
slôz in die îsenhalten.
dô die zwêne alten   3250
daz hiuselîn gesâhen,
ze sælden si des jâhen
daz si dâ nâch ir unmaht
geruowen müesen die naht.
   Gevüeret hâten si mit in
die spîse (daz was ein schœner sin)
der sie bedorften zuo der nôt,
beidiu wîn unde brôt
und dar zuo swaz in tohte
daz man gevüeren mohte.   3260
des emphie der vischære
mit vreuden âne swære
die wol berâten geste.
er sach wol unde weste
er möhtẹ ir wol geniezen:
des enwoldẹ in niht verdriezen,
er enschüefẹ in rîchen gemach,
wandẹ er si wol berâten sach.
daz tet er mêre umbẹ ir guot
dan durch sînen milten muot.   3270
er emphie si baz dan den gast
dem des guotes gebrast,
Grêgôrjum den reinen man:
in dûhte da enwære niht nutzes an.

Grass-covered was this path that led
Unbeaten far out on a head
Of land where dwelt, quite close to shore,
The fisher I've described before—   3240
The very fisher who had bestowed
So rude a welcome in his abode
Upon the blessed man in need,
The one who did the evil deed
With malice, causing Gregory
To sit upon the cliff at sea—
So wild, so desolate, so bare
(And to this day he still sat there)—
Locking his legs in iron fast.
Now when the two old men at last   3250
The fisher's little hut espied,
They felt Good Fortune at their side,
That they in their exhausted plight
Could now find rest there for the night.
    They carried with them such provision
(To do so was a wise decision)
As in emergency they'd need,
Both of bread and wine; indeed,
They carried with them everything
Of use to them that they could bring.   3260
The fisherman for this was glad.
A welcome without qualm he bade
These well-provided guests. From them,
He full well realized, could stem
A goodly profit for him, too.
He spared himself no pains to do
All for their ease without demur,
On seeing how well stocked they were.
Their wealth caused him to play this part,
And not the kindness of his heart.   3270
These guests he welcomed better than
He'd welcomed once that wealthless man,
Gregorius, the good. He'd thought
From him the profit would be naught.

Dô si gewunnen guot gemach,
der vischære zen gesten sprach:
'mir ist harte wol geschehen,
sît ich hie solde gesehen
alsus guote liute:
ich hân gevangen hiute   3280
einen harte schœnen visch.'
sus wart er ûf einen tisch
vür die herren geleit.
nu enhâte er niht misseseit,
wandę er was lanc unde grôz:
des er vil gerne genôz
an den phenningen.
dâ wart ein kurzez dingen:
si hiezen in im gelten sâ.
nû bâten si in dâ   3290
den wirt selben gellen.
do begundę er in zevellen,
daz siz alle sâhen an.
dô vant der schazgîre man
den slüzzel in sînem magen,
von dem ir ê hôrtet sagen,
dâ er Grêgôrjum mite
beslôz mit unsüezem site
vor sibenzehen jâren ê
unde warf in in den sê   3300
und sprach, ze swelher stunde
er den slüzzel vunde
ûz des meres ünde,
sô wærę er âne sünde.
dô er in in dem vische vant,
dô erkandę er sich zehant
wie er getobet hâte
und vie sich alsô drâte
mit beiden handen in daz hâr.

In a remarkable way, the key to Gregorius' fetters is restored.

Now to his guests, when they had shed
Their weariness, the fisher said:
"A lucky thing occurred to me,
Considering that I should see
Distinguished men like you appear.
Fortunate that, since you're here,   3280
A handsome fish this day I've caught!"
And so to a table it was brought
And put before the noblemen.
No lie it was he'd told them then,
For long and heavy was the fish.
To enjoy it was his wish
By means of coins in plenitude;
And not much bargaining ensued.
That he be paid immediately*
Was their command, and then that he,   3290
Their host, himself remove the gall.*
While he cut it open, all,
Watching him, were standing round.
Then the coin-greedy fisher found
Within the maw that very key
You've heard about before from me,
The key that he had used to lock
Gregorius cruelly to that rock
Years ago, fourteen and three,
And that he'd hurled into the sea,   3300
With the words that, when he'd find
Again the key he'd just consigned
Unto the waters of the sea,
Of sin Gregorius would be free.
When he thus found and recognized
The key, the fisher realized
How senselessly he'd acted there,
And fell to tearing at his hair
With both his hands. Now I tell you,

ich hetę im geholfen vür wâr,   3310
und wærę ich im gewesen bî,
swie erbolgen ich im anders sî.
   Dô er sich geroufte gnuoc
und sich zen brüsten gesluoc,
dô vrâcten in die herren
waz im möhte gewerren,
dô sị in sô tiure sâhen klagen.
nu begundę er in vil rehte sagen
um Grêgôrjum sînen gast,
daz in des mæres niht gebrast.   3320
ich wænę ez unnütze wære,
ob ich daz vorder mære
iu nû aber anderstunt
mit ganzen worten tæte kunt:
sô wurden einer rede zwô.
die boten wurden harte vrô,
wan si spürten an dem mære
daz ez der selbe wære
an den in got selbe riet
und in ze bâbest beschiet.   3330
   Dô er in beiden glîche
alsô offenlîche
sîne bîhte getete,
ir vüeze suochtę er mit bete,
daz si im etelîchen rât
tæten vür die missetât.
dô si die grôzen riuwe
mit geistlîcher triuwe
gesâhen an dem armen,
nu begundę er si erbarmen   3340
und gehiezen si im daz,
er möhte vil deste baz
komen von sînem meine,
ob er si zuo dem steine
des morgens wolde wîsen.
nû sâhen im die grîsen
diu ougen über wallen,

If I'd been with him then, it's true,   3310
I'd have had to sympathize
Despite my anger otherwise.
    Since he continued without rest
To tear his hair and beat his breast,
The nobles, seeing the extent
Of the fisherman's lament,
Asked him what disturbed him thus.
About his guest, Gregorius,
In full detail he then explained,
So that a true account they gained.   3320
For me now to repeat anew
The first part of this tale to you
In every single word, would be
Superfluous, I think: you see,
A twice-told tale I'd then impart.
The messengers rejoiced at heart,
For from these words they realized
He was the man God had advised
They go to seek; for it was he
That should be pope by God's decree.   3330
    Upon confessing to the two,*
And telling both all that he knew
So openly, the fisher then
Cast himself down before the men,
Imploring help that he be shown
How for his sin he might atone.
The noblemen, upon the sight
Of the fisher, so contrite,
Felt pity for the poor man's pain
And pious devotion in its train;   3340
They promised him that the best way
His true remorse he could display,
To be freed of his offense,
Was, in the morn, to take them hence
And lead them to the desolate stone.
The wise old men saw tears that shone
And glistened hot as they would rise

die heizen zeher vallen
über sînen grâwen bart.
er sprach: 'waz tuoc uns diu vart ?   3350
vil wol wîse ich iuch dar:
die vart verliese wir gar.
ich weiz wol, erst nû lange tôt.
ich lie in in maniger nôt
ûf dem wilden steine:
hæte er der niuwan eine,
ez enmöhte dehein lîp erwern.
ir endürfet dingen noch gern
daz wir in lebenden vinden:
enwære er von kalten winden   3360
und von vroste niht verderbet,
der hunger hete in ersterbet.'
nu erkanden si den gotes gewalt
sô starken und sô manicvalt,
ob er sîn geruochte phlegen,
daz in harte wol sîn segen
gevriste vor aller vreise.
ûf die kurzen reise
sô wart er tiure gemant:
die gelobete er in ze hant.   3370

Des morgenes vil vruo
kêrten si dem steine zuo.
dô si mit arbeiten
die boume zuo bereiten
daz si ûf den stein kâmen
und des war nâmen
wâ Grêgôrjus wære,
der lebende marterære:
einen harte schœnen man
dem vil lützel iender an   3380
hunger oder vrost schein

And well within the fisher's eyes
And fall on his gray beard below.
"What use is it for us to go? 3350
I'd gladly lead you there," said he,
"But all in vain the trip would be.
I well know that he's long since dead;
For when from that lone cliff I sped,
I left him there in many a need.
And had he been of all needs freed
Save one, he could not have endured.
You have no ground to feel assured
Or hope we'll find him still alive.
If he'd been able to survive 3360
The bite of frost and cold winds' breath,
He would have died starvation's death."
    Now they knew God's power of old
To be so mighty and manifold,
If to protect him God had deigned,
God's blessing well might have sustained
And kept him from all danger free.
And so the fisher solemnly
Was urged the short trip to pursue.
At once he promised this he'd do. 3370

        The fisherman takes the Roman legates to the
    island cliff where they discover Gregorius.

    In the early dawn next day,
Towards the cliff they made their way.
With effort each then used his oar
To pole* the bark onto the shore;
They climbed the cliff and tried to see
Where Gregorius might be.
On looking round they there beheld
How that living martyr dwelled.
Perhaps you think what met their eyes*
Was quite a handsome man, nowise 3380
In need? a man on whom were lost

oder armuot dehein,
von zierlîchem geræte
an lîbe und an der wæte,
daz nieman deheine
von edelem gesteine,
von sîden und von golde
bezzer haben solde,
wol ze wunsche gesniten,
der mit lachenden siten,   3390
mit gelphen ougen gienge
und liebe vriunt emphienge,
mit goltvarwen hâre,
daz iuch in zewâre
ze sehenne luste harte,
mit wol geschorenem barte,
in allen wîs alsô getân
als er ze tanze solde gân,
mit sô gelîmter beinwât
sô si zer werlde beste stât,   3400
den envunden si niender dâ:
er mohte wol wesen anderswâ.
    Ich sage iu waz si vunden.
do si suochen begunden
ûf dem wilden steine,
der guote und der reine
der wart ir schiere innen.
nû wolde er in entrinnen,
wan sîn schame diu was grôz:
er was nacket unde blôz.   3410
nu enmohte er niht loufen drâte,
wande er gebende hâte
an ietwederem beine.
er viel zuo dem steine:
sus wolde er sich verborgen hân.
dô er si sach zuo im gân,
dô brach er vür die schame ein krût.
sus vunden si den gotes trût,
einen dürftigen ûf der erde,

All signs of hunger or of frost?
In person so magnificent,
And in his dress so opulent
That finer nowhere could be had
Than that in which he would be clad?
His jewelry, silks, and gold would seem
So beautiful that one would deem
Him cut to perfect elegance?
With happy gait he would advance,　　　　3390
With shining eyes he then would walk
To greet dear friends with kindly talk?
His hair the color of pure gold
And so lovely to behold,
You'd have rejoiced at sight of it?
His well-trimmed beard so exquisite!
In every way behaving so,
As if a-dancing he would go?
His trunkhose fitting him so tight
Just as society deems right?—　　　　3400
Well, this man they found nowhere there;
This man they might have found elsewhere.
　　I'll tell you what it was they found.
When they began to search the ground
Upon the desolate cliff, that man,
Both good and pure, straightway began
To realize their presence near.
He wished to flee and not appear
Before them in his nakedness,
So great his shame and his distress.　　　　3410
He was not able to make haste
To run away, for bonds embraced
And shackled both his legs, so that
Upon the stone he fell down flat,
Intending thus concealed to lie.
But as he saw them coming nigh,
With leaves he covered what was bare.
Thus God's beloved they found there:
Poor and destitute on earth,

ze gote in hôhem werde,   3420
den liuten widerzæme,
ze himele vil genæme.
　Der arme was zewâre
erwahsen von dem hâre,
verwalken zuo der swarte,
an houbet und an barte:
ê was ez ze rehte reit,
nû ruozvar von der arbeit.
ê wâren im diu wangen
mit rœte bevangen   3430
mit gemischeter wîze
und veiz mit guotem vlîze,
nû swarz und in gewichen,
daz antlütze erblichen.
ê wâren im vür wâr
diu ougen gelph unde klâr,
der munt ze vreuden gestalt,
nû bleich unde kalt,
diu ougen tief trüebe rôt,
als ez der mangel gebôt,   3440
mit brâwen behangen
rûhen unde langen,
ê grôz zen liden allen
daz vleisch, nû zuo gevallen
unz an daz gebeine:
er was sô glîche kleine
an beinen und an armen,
ez möhte got erbarmen.
　Dâ im diu îsenhalte lac
beidiu naht unde tac,   3450
dâ hete si im ob dem vuoze
daz vleisch harte unsuoze
unz an daz bein vernozzen,
sô daz si was begozzen
mit bluote zallen stunden
von den vrischen wunden.
daz was sîn swerende arbeit,

In God's esteem of highest worth;   3420
Repugnant here to mortal men,
In Heaven a pleasing denizen.
    There he was, poor man, uncouth,
Overgrown with hair, in truth,
That hung from head and face and chin
And matted to his very skin.
Hs well-groomed locks of former time
Were soot-colored and full of grime.
In times gone by his cheeks had known
A pleasing plumpness and had shown   3430
In contrast charming to the sight
A rosy hue mingled with white.
But dark and hollow were they now,
And pallid grown his face and brow.
The truth to tell, in former days
His eyes shone clear with sparkling gaze;
His warm mouth once of joyous mold,
Now was colorless and cold.
By need and circumstance ill used,
His eyes grown somber, deep, suffused   3440
With red, and over them hung now
Long, shaggy tufts from each eyebrow.
Formerly his every limb
With solid flesh was firm and trim;
But he was shrunken to the bone.
So uniformly thin had grown
His legs and arms that at this sight
God must have pitied his poor plight.
    Now since within that iron chain
Night and day he fast had lain,   3450
The iron had cut gruesomely
Above his feet to such degree
That quite consumed was all the flesh
Down to the bone; and ever afresh
From open and raw wounds there drained
The blood that red his shackles stained.
This foul affliction, festering sore,

âne̜ ander nôt die er leit.
ich gelîche̜ in disen sachen,
als der ein lîlachen   3460
über dorne spreite:
man möhte̜ im sam gereite
allez sîn gebeine
grôz unde kleine
haben gezalt durch sîne hût.
swie sêre der gotes trût
an dem lîbe wære
verwandelt von der swære,
nû was der heilige geist
dar an gewesen sîn volleist   3470
alsô ganzlichen
daz im niht was entwichen,
er enhæte sîn alten
kunst unz her behalten
von worten und von buochen.
die in dâ vuoren suochen,
als in die hâten gesehen,
als ich iu nû hân verjehen,
des lîbes alsô armen,
do begunde̜ er in erbarmen   3480
sô sêre daz der ougen vlôz
regens wîs ir wât begôz.
si beswuoren in bî gote
und bî sînem gebote
daz er si wizzen lieze
ob er Grêgôrjus hieze.
dô er sô tiure wart gemant,
dô tet er in bekant
daz erz Grêgôrjus wære.
nû sageten si im diu mære,   3490
war umbe si ûz wæren komen,
als ir ê habet vernomen,
als in des nahtes beiden
von gote wart bescheiden,
daz er in hæte genant,

Was his besides all else he bore.

   If on a thorn bush one had spread
A sheet of linen, I'd have said   3460
There'd be a likeness in this respect:
One could as easily detect
Gregorius' bones, both large and small,
And through his skin take count of all
As through the linen count each thorn.

   No matter how his flesh was torn,
How God's beloved had altered quite
In body through his grievous plight—
Throughout the years the Holy Ghost
Had helped him to the uttermost   3470
With such support that to this day
He had forfeited in no way
His old proficiency and skill,*
But had command of language still,
And had retained all that he'd learned.
When those who sought him there discerned
His form, so pitiful to view,
As I have just described to you,
So strong did their compassion grow
That heavy tears began to flow   3480
From their eyes and fall the more
Like rain upon the clothes they wore.
They adjured him by the Lord,
By His Commandments they implored,
That he inform them and proclaim
Whether Gregory were his name.

   Entreated thus so solemnly,
He granted them their urgent plea
And said he was Gregorius.
They told him then their marvelous   3490
And strange tale, that you full well know,
Of how they'd journeyed forth—since so
They'd been instructed by the Light
Of God Himself during the night—
That God had chosen him alone

selbẹ erwelt und erkant
und ze rihtære gesat
hie en erde an sîn selbes stat.

    Als er die botschaft vernam,
wie nâhenz sînem herzen kam!   3500
dô sancte der gotes werde
daz houbet zuo der erde.
mit manigem trahen er sprach,
daz er si nie an gesach:
'sît ir kristen liute,
sô êret got hiute
und gât vil drâte von mir,
wandẹ ich der êren wol enbir
daz mir diu gnâde iht geschehe
daz ich iemen guoter an sehe   3510
mit so süntlîchen ougen.
gotẹ enist daz niht tougen:
mîn vleisch ist sô unreine
daz ich billich eine
belîbe unz an mînen tôt.
daz mir der êwigen nôt
diu sêle über werde,
daz koufẹ ich ûf der erde.
wærẹ ich bî in hiute,
ez müesen guote liute   3520
engelten mîner missetât,
sô hôhe sô mîn schulde stât.
sô möhte boum unde gras
und swaz ie grüenes bî mir was
dorren von der grimme
mîner unreinen stimme
und von der unsüeze
mîner baren vüeze.
und daz der süezen weter gruoz

And named him judge upon the throne,
And designated him as head,
To reign on earth in the Lord's stead.

Gregorius is persuaded by the legates and the
fisherman to leave the cliff.

Now when their message he had heard,
How deeply was his heart then stirred!   3500
As heavy tears began to flow,*
The godly man with head bent low
To earth, and never a glance their way,
Thereupon began to say:
"If you are truly Christians, aye,
God today you'll glorify
If you get quickly gone from me:
For I'm not worthy assuredly
Of being granted so much grace
As to look on a good man's face   3510
With such sinful eyes as mine.
This is not hidden from God Divine:
My flesh and blood are so impure
That rightly I shall here endure
Alone, until my day of death.
On earth I must with every breath
Strive to save my soul, to gain
Redemption from eternal pain.
If I lived among men today,
The innocent would have to pay*   3520
In suffering for my sinful state.
    "The guilt I carry is so great,
Each blade of grass and every tree,
Whatever there was of green near me,
Would wither and wilt at the wild tone
My unclean voice now calls its own;
And all would perish that's clean and sweet,
Touched by the foulness of my feet!
That the sweet greeting of the air

dâ von diu werlt gestân muoz   3530
und diu heimlîche linde
von regen und von winde
mir sint alsô gemeine
als ob ich wære reine,
daz der liehten sunnen schîn
sô diemüete geruochet sîn
daz er mich volleclichen an
schînet als einen man,
der gnâden wære mîn vleisch unwert.
daz ir mîn ze meister gert,   3540
daz ist ein erdâhter spot.
ich hân umbe unsern herren got
verdienet leider verre baz
sînen zornlîchen haz
dan daz er an mich kêre
die gnâde und die êre
die ein bâbest haben sol.
man enbirt mîn ze Rôme wol:
iu wære ze mir niht wol geschehen.
muget ir doch mînen lîp sehen?   3550
der ist sô ungenæme,
den êren widerzæme.
wart mir ie herren vuore kunt,
der ist vergezzen ze dirre stunt.
ich bin der liute ungewon:
den bin ich billichen von.
ir herren, nemet selbe war,
mir sint verwandelet vil gar
der sin, der lîp und die site
die dem von rehte wonent mite   3560
der grôzes gewaltes phlegen sol:
ich enzime ze bâbest niht wol.
vil sæligen liute,
nû lât mir daz hiute
zeinem heile sîn geschehen
daz ir mich hie habet gesehen
und geruochet iuch erbarmen

(Where mankind is, it must be there),   3530
And the familiar gentleness
Of soft rain and mild wind's caress,
That these should keep me company
As if I were of all sin free—
And that the clear light of the sun,
As it does for anyone,
Deigns with such humility
To shine abundantly on me—
Such grace my flesh does not deserve.
That as your master I should serve   3540
You have contrived as mockery.
From our Lord God, unhappily,
I have deserved it far the more
That He in anger me abhor
Than that He now bestow on me
The grace and honored dignity
That are due a pope. Rome well
Can do without me; truth to tell,
You'd be ill served to have me there.
To see my body, if you'd care,   3550
Would make your loathing so intense,
It would repel all reverence.
If noble manners I have known,
I've now forotten them. I own,
To men I'm not habituated;
From them I'm justly separated.
For you, yourselves, my lords, now see
How conduct, mind, and body in me
Have chánged from what should be, by right,
Inherent in one who great might   3560
And power must wield. I am not fit
As pope upon the throne to sit.
   "O you blessed company,
To my salvation may it be
That it has come to pass today
That you have seen me here; and may
You feel compassionate toward me,

über mich vil armen
und gedenket mîn ze gote.
wir haben von sînem gebote,   3570
swer umbe den sündære bite,
dâ lœse er sich selben mite.
nu ist zît daz wir uns scheiden:
waz vrumet iu daz beiden?
ir vreut an mir des tiuvels muot.
mîn kurzwîle ist alze guot.
ich bûwe hie zewâre
in dem sibenzehenden jâre,
daz ich nie menschen gesach.
ich vürhte, vreude und der gemach   3580
diu ich mit rede mit iu hie hân,
ich müeze ir ze buoze stân
vor im der deheine missetât
ungerochen niene lât.'
     Sus stuont er ûf und wolde dan.
do beswuoren in die zwêne man
alsô verre bî gote
und sînem vorhtlîchen gebote
daz er doch stille gesaz
und hôrte ir rede vürbaz.   3590
nû buten si im beide
mit triuwen und mit eide
der rede solhe sicherheit
diu im dâ was vür geleit
daz er si geloubete baz.
er sprach: 'ich was ein vollez vaz
süntlîcher schanden,
dô ich mit disen banden
gestetent wart ûf disen stein,
diu ir hie sehent um mîniu bein.   3600
[diu ich hie trage mit sorgen.
dô wart alsus geborgen
der slüzzel dâ mit ich dar in
alsô vaste versperret bin:
der wart geworfen in den sê.

Sinful man though I may be,
Remembering me when you pray
To God. The Lord's Commandments say: 3570
Who for the sinner intercedes*
Saves himself as to God he pleads.
It's time for you to go your way.
What use for both of you to stay,
And through me make the Devil glad?
The pastime that I just have had
Is far too pleasant. For I have spent
My seventeenth year in banishment,
And of mankind I've here seen none.
The joy and pleasure I have won,   3580
I fear, in talking here with you,
I must do penance for anew
To Him Who no misdeed at all
Will leave unpunished, great or small."
    He rose and wished to go away.*
The two implored him then to stay;
So long did both in God's name sue,
And by God's dread Commandments, too,
That he remained there quietly
And listened to their further plea.   3590
In all sincerity they both
Attested to him under oath,
Assuring him, as best they knew,
That every word they said was true,
So that he trusted them at last.
    "A shameful vessel in the past
Was I," he said, "with sins ingrained,
And full of faults, when I was chained
Upon this rock with lock and key,
My legs in gyves that you now see.   3600
In sorrow I those bonds endure.
Then the key that made secure
My fetters, locking me that day
Within them, was concealed this way:
Into the sea the key was thrown,

der in dar warf der sprach niht mê,
wan sô er in vünde,
sô wærę ich âne sünde.]
nu ist niemens sünde alsô grôz,
des gewalt die hellę entslôz,   3610
des gnâde sî noch merre.
ob got unser herre
mîner manigen missetât
durch sînen trôst vergezzen hât
und ob ich reine worden bin,
des muoz er uns drin
ein rehtez wortzeichen geben
oder sich muoz mîn leben
ûf disem steine enden.
er muoz mir wider senden   3620
den slüzzel dâ mit ich dâ bin
sus vaste beslozzen in
oder ich gerûmez niemer hie.'
    Nû viel der vischærę an diu knie
mit manigem trahen vür in,
er sprach: 'vil lieber herrę, ich bin
der selbe sündige man
der sich verworhte dar an.
ich arme verlorne
ich emphie iuch mit zorne.   3630
diz was diu wirtschaft die ich iu bôt:
ich gap iu schelten vür daz brôt,
ich schancte iu ze vlîze
mit manigem itewîze.
sus behielt ich iuch ein naht
mit unwirdę und mit grôzem braht.
alsus bin ich worden alt
daz ich der sünde nie engalt.
ez ist der sêle noch gespart:
ich engenieze danne dirre vart   3640
die ich her mit triuwen hân getân,
sô sol ichs vol ze buoze stân.
darnâch volctę ich iuwer bete,

And he who threw it said, alone
If he should ever find the key
Would I then of sin be free.
Yet there is no one's sin so great
But that His grace Who forced Hell's gate*   3610
Wide open is far greater still.
But if it is our Lord God's will
To show that He has now forgiven
My many crimes, and I've been shriven
And by the Holy Ghost made pure,
Then a token, true and sure,
Let Him give to the three of us;*
If not, I'll spend my life here thus
Upon this cliff until the end.
That very key let Him now send   3620
To me again that in the past
Locked me within my chains so fast,
Or else I'll never leave this place."
    As tears rolled down the fisher's face,
He knelt before Gregorius
And bending low addressed him thus,
"Dear lord, I am the same man who
Sinned so greatly against you.
O lost soul that I am, I gave
The welcome of an angry knave.   3630
This was my hospitality:
For bread I served you mockery;
For drink I filled your glass with jeers,
With scorn, reproaches, and with sneers.
I gave you shelter for a night
With loud contempt and grudging spite.
And here am I, and old I've grown,
But for that sin did not atone.
Still for my crime my soul must pay.
Unless my journey here today   3640
In good faith bring me benefit,
My soul will suffer in full for it.
I then did what you asked of me,

wan daz ichs in hônschaft tete:
ich brâhte iuch ûf disen stein.
alsus beslôz ich iuwer bein
und warf den slüzzel in den sê.
ich engedâhtẹ an iuch niemer mê
unz gester mîn sündigiu hant
den slüzzel in einem vische vant.   3650
daz sâhen die herren wol,
ob ichz mit in erziugen sol.'
   Er entslôz die îsenhalten.
dô teilten die alten
mit im ir phäflîchiu kleit:
und als er an wart geleit,
dô vuorten si mit in dan
disen sündelôsen man
ab dem wilden steine.
nû was vil harte kleine   3660
sînes armen lîbes maht.
nû beliben si die naht
mit dem vischære.
des jâmer was vil swære:
er suochte buoze unde rât
um die grôzen missetât
die er vor an im begie,
do er in sô hœnlîchẹ emphie.
nû wuosch diu grôze triuwe
und diu ganze riuwe   3670
und der ougen ünde
den vlecken sîner sünde,
daz im diu sêle genas.

   Dannoch dô Grêgôrjus was
in der sünden gewalt,
als iu dâ vor was gezalt,
dô er von sîm gewalte gie

Save that I did it mockingly.
I brought you out upon this rock
And bound you fast with chain and lock.
Into the sea the key I threw,
And never again gave thought to you
Till yesterday from a fish's maw
My sinful hand this key did draw.   3650
These nobles saw it all, and I
Can call on them to testify."

   The iron shackles he took off,
While the old men began to doff
Their priestly garb to share with him.
When they had clothed his every limb,
Their journey back they then began,
And led with them this sinless man
Down from the desolate rock to shore.
Now his poor body, weak and sore,   3660
Had little strength in its sad plight;
And so they rested for the night
At the fisherman's. So great
His grief, so sorrowful his state,
The fisher, in deep penitence,
Sought to atone for his offence
In having welcomed Gregory
Long ago so scornfully.
Now his great earnestness, the force
Of his complete and true remorse,   3670
The flood of unchecked tears that fell,
Cleansed him of taint of sin as well,
And his immortal soul was saved.

   The long-lost tablet is wondrously found, and
   Gregorius consents to leave for Rome.

   While Gregory was still enslaved
And in the power of sin held fast
(As has been told you in the past)—
When from his lordly realm he went,

und in der vischære emphie
in sînem hûs sô swache
und in mit ungemache   3680
des nahtes sô wol beriet,
morgen dô er danne schiet
und er der tavele vergaz:
die wîle er ûf dem steine saz,
so gemuote in nie mêre
dehein dinc alsô sêre.
nû gedâhte er aber dar an
und manden vischenden man
daz er durch got tæte,
ob er si vunden hæte,   3690
daz si im wider würde,
daz sîner sünden bürde
deste ringer wære.
dô sprach der vischære:
'leider ich engesach si nie.
nû saget, wâ liezet ir si hie,
oder wie vergâzet ir ir sus?'
'ich lie si', sprach Grêgôrjus,
'in dem hiuselîne dâ ich slief.
dô man mir des morgens rief,   3700
dô wart mîn angest swære
daz ich versûmet wære:
ich erschrihte von slâfe und îlte iu nâch
und wart mir leider alsô gâch
daz ich der tavele vergaz.'
der vischære sprach: 'waz hülfe uns daz
ob wir si suochten? dâ si lît,
dâ ist si vûl vor maniger zît.
ouwê, lieber herre mîn,
jâ stuont daz selbe hiuselîn   3710
nâch iu niht zwelf wochen
unz daz ez wart zebrochen:
ich hân ez allez verbrant,
beidiu dach unde want.
ich truoc iu dô sô herten muot:

And when the fisher in insolent,
Degrading manner welcomed him,
Offering shelter that was grim,　　　　　　　3680
In his mean hut, for that one night,
And he forgot at dawn's first light
To take his tablet when he went—
In all the time that he had spent
On the cliff, naught pained his mind
More than that tablet left behind.
Now again he thought of it.
Exhorting the fisher to admit
If he had found it, he implored
That the tablet be restored　　　　　　　　3690
For God's sake to him at this time,
So that the burden of his crime
Would then that much the lighter be.
　　The fisher said, "Unhappily,
I never saw it. Tell me, now,
Where did you leave it? or say how
You happened to forget it here?"
"I left it," Gregory said, "quite near,
Within the small hut where I lay,
When I was called early that day.　　　　　3700
So great was my anxiety
That were I late you'd not take me,
That, startled from sleep, at once I raced,
Forgetting the tablet in my haste,
Alas, as after you I sped."
"What use if we," the fisher said,
"Should search the place where it was laid?
Long since it will have there decayed.
Alas, O my dear lord, O woe!
Scarce twelve weeks after you did go　　　3710
Did that same little hut still stand
Before it was torn down. My hand
Set fire to it. I let it all
Burn down entire, yes, roof and wall.
My heart toward you was then so hard

unde wærez gewesen guot
vür wint oder vür regen,
ir enwæret dâ inne niht gelegen.
dâ ê daz hiuselîn was,
dâ wahset nu unbederbe gras,   3720
nezzelen und unkrût.'
    Do ersiufte der gotes trût:
got er im sô helfen bat,
er enkæme niemer von der stat,
ob er ir niht vunde.
nû giengen si zestunde
mit gabelen und mit rechen
und begunden nâher brechen
daz unkrût und den mist.
nu erzeicte der dâ gnædic ist   3730
an dem guoten Grêgôrjô
ein vil grôzez zeichen dô,
wandę er sîne tavel vant
als niuwę als si von sîner hant
vüere der si dâ worhte.
vreude unde vorhte،
heten die daz sâhen:
weinde si des jâhen,
diz wærę ein sælic man.
dâ enlugen si niht an.   3740

    Dô des morgens ir vart
gegen Rômę erhaben wart,
dô sâhen sį dicke under wegen
daz der gereite gotes segen
disse reinen mannes phlac
mit vlîze naht unde tac.
si engeruorte ûf der reise
nie dehein wegevreise:

That, could the hut have offered guard
Or shelter against the wind or rain,
In it you never would have lain.
Where once that small hut stood, alas,
The earth bears only useless grass,   3720
And weeds among the nettles hide."
    The man, beloved of God, then sighed.
He prayed for aid and then maintained,
Unless the tablet he regained,
So help him God, there he would stay.
Now they betook themselves straightway,
Each with a weeding-hoe or rake,
To clear the rank grass and to break
The rubbish loose and dig below.
Then did the Gracious One bestow   3730
Upon the good man, Gregory,
A wondrous token for all to see.
He found his tablet, and behold!
It was as new as when of old
Its maker fashioned it fresh and clear.
Joy combined with awesome fear
Filled the hearts of all those there;
Nor could they, as they wept, forbear
Avowing him as holy—aye,
In saying so, they did not lie.   3740

    The holiness of Gregorius is shown on the jour-
    ney to Rome. He is crowned pope and becomes a
    great spiritual force.

    Now in the morning the next day
To Rome they started on their way,
And as they traveled they could see
How God's blessing abundantly
Cared for this pure man in each way
Solicitously both night and day;
For not one dangerous episode
Threatened them upon the road.

ir spîsę erschôz in alsô wol
daz ir vaz alwege wâren vol,   3750
swie vil si drûz genâmen,
unz si ze Rôme kâmen.
    Von einen gnâden ich iu sage.
vor der kunft drîer tage
dô wart ze Rômę ein michel schal:
sich begunden über al
die glocken selbe liuten
und kunten den liuten
daz ir rihtære
schiere künftic wære.   3760
dâ kôs wîp unde man
sîne heilikeit wol an.
si vuoren gegen im sâ
engegen Equitânjâ
die drîe tageweide.
si hâten über heide
einen gotlîchen ruom:
si truogen ir heiltuom,
wüllîn unde barvuoz.
er hôrte williclîchen gruoz   3770
an sînem antvange
mit lobe und mit sange.
ez lâgen ûf der strâze
siechen âne mâze:
die kâmen dar ûf sînen trôst,
daz si würden erlôst.
der ernerte sîn segen
harte manigen under wegen.
swen er dâ beruorte,
dâ man in hin vuorte,   3780
sîn guot wille oder sîn hant,
sîn wort oder sîn gewant,
der wart dâ ze dirre stunt
von sînem kumber gesunt.
Rôme diu mære
emphie ir rihtære

Their stores were constantly renewed:
Whatever they used of drink or food,   3750
Abundance served at each repast
Until they entered Rome at last.

One grace of God I'll now declare:
Three days before his advent there,
In Rome a wondrous ringing soared
On high; as of their own accord,
Long and loud the bells all pealed,
And to the people this revealed
That their sovereign regent here
On earth for them would soon appear.   3760
Men and women, thus apprized,
His holiness all realized.
Forth they went without delay
To meet him on his holy way.
Three days they walked toward Aquitaine*
With pomp across the open plain.
Barefoot, clad in wool, they went
In long procession, penitent,*
Their shrine of relics held on high.
As jubilant the throng drew nigh,   3770
In welcoming hymns of praise he heard
Their readiness to serve his word.

Numberless on the broad highway
The sick, the crippled, the lepers lay
Who sought his help to make them free
Of their sore calamity.
And on the road his blessing healed
Great numbers who to him appealed.
It did not matter whom they brought him,
The lame, the halt, the blind that sought him,   3780
If he but touched them with his cloak,
His hand, or if he greeting spoke,
Or if his good will they secured,
Straightway of sickness each was cured.

The Eternal City, glorious Rome,
Welcomed her new sovereign home

mit lachendem muote.
daz kam ir zallem guote:
wandez enwart dâ ze stat
nie bâbest gesat   3790
der baz ein heilære
der sêle wunden wære.

Er kunde wol ze rehte leben,
wan im diu mâze was gegeben
vons heiligen geistes lêre.
des rehten huotẹ er sêre.
ez ist reht daz man behalte
diemüetẹ in gewalte
(dâ genesent die armen mite)
und sol doch vrävellîche site   3800
durch die vorhtẹ erzeigen
und die mit rehte neigen
die wider dem rehten sint.
ob aber ein des tiuvels kint
durch die stôle niene tuo,
dâ hœret danne gewalt zuo.
des sint diu zwei gerihte guot:
si lêrent reht, slahent hôhen muot.
man sol dem sündære
ringen sîne swære   3810
mit senfter buoze,
daz im diu riuwe suoze.
daz reht ist alsô swære,
swer dem sündære
ze vaste wil nâch jagen,
daz enmac der lîp niht wol vertragen.
ob er genâde suochen wil,
gît man im gâhes buoze vil,
vil lîhtẹ ein man dâ von verzaget,
daz er sich aber gotẹ entsaget   3820
und wirt wider des tiuvels kneht.
dâ von gât gnâde vür daz reht.
sus kundẹ er rehte mâze geben
über geistlîchez leben,

With joyful heart; and this man's reign
Brought her all benefit and gain;
For never had the Holy See
Been ruled by better pope than he,   3790
A true physician who could heal
Wounds of the soul with holy zeal.
   He lived a just life and serene
According to the golden mean
The Holy Ghost to him revealed.
He was justice's strong shield.
Men who wield power mightily
Should exercise humility
(One can help the poor this way),
And yet a resolute will display,   3800
Rousing apprehensive awe
To make men rightly yield to law
Who scorn both justice and rectitude.
If someone's of the Devil's brood
And for the *stole** shows no respect,
With force that man must needs be checked.
Both modes of passing sentence alike
Are good: they teach the right, and strike
Inordinate pride. The sinner's pack
Should be made lighter for his back: 3810
For if his penance is not too grim,
Contrition may grow sweet for him.
Justice alone is so austere,
If with a sinner one's too severe,
His body will not endure the strain:
Through persecution there's no gain.
If a man for mercy plead,
And rashly penance is decreed
Too burdensome, he may lose heart,
A second time from God depart,   3820
And once more join the Devil's band.
Hence mercy leads justice by the hand.
   With such just fitness did he reign
Over the spiritual domain*

dâ mite der sündære genas
und der guote stæte was.
von sîner starken lêre
sô wuohs diu gotes êre
vil harte starclîche
in rœmischem rîche.   3830

That the sinner's soul was saved,
And the good steadfast behaved.
Through the force of what he taught
Great glory unto God he brought,
That His praise grew from day to day
Wherever Roman rule held sway.   3830

Sîn muoter, sîn base, sîn wîp
(diu driu heten einen lîp),
dô si in Equitânjam
von dem bâbest vernam
daz er sô garwe wære
ein trôst der sündære,
dô suochte si in durch rât
umbẹ ir houbetmissetât,
daz si der sünden bürde
von im entladen würde.   3840
unde dô si in gesach
und im ir bîhte vor gesprach,
nû was dem guoten wîbe
vons bâbestes lîbe
ein unkundez mære
daz er ir sun wære:
ouch hete si an sich geleit
die riuwe und die arbeit,
sît si sich schieden beide,
daz ir der lîp von leide   3850
entwichen was begarwe
an krefte und an varwe,
daz er ir niht erkande
unz si sich im nande
undz lant Equitânjam.

CHAPTER VI

Mother and Son Are Reunited

Gregorius' mother comes to Rome to seek the
pope's aid. He recognizes her and reveals himself to her as her son.

When his mother, his aunt, his wife
(The three were one, with but one life),
Far away in Aquitaine,
Heard it said in her domain
That for a sinner's soul the pope
Was complete solace, comfort, hope,
Off she went to him to win
Advice about her mortal sin,
And have him lighten the oppression
Of the weight of her transgression.   3840
When she her eyes upon him laid,
And her confession to him made,
The good woman, as she sat there,
Was, in truth, quite unaware
That this holy pope was one
Who was none other than her son.
Now sore penance she had placed
On herself, and toil embraced
Since from the other each had gone,
And had grown frail and weak and wan   3850
Through suffering; and now at length,
She lacked all coloring and strength,
So that he knew her not again
Until she spoke her name, and then
To Aquitaine's domain referred.

dô er ir bîhte vernam,
(dô enbejach si im anders niht
niuwan der selben geschiht
diu im ouch ê was kunt),
dô erkande er zestunt   3860
daz si sîn muoter wære.
der guote und der gewære
der vreute sich ze gote,
daz si sînem gebote
alsô verre under lac:
wande er sach wol daz si phlac
riuwe und rehter buoze.
mit williclîchem gruoze
emphie er sîne muoter dô
und was des herzenlichen vrô   3870
daz im diu sælde geschach
daz er si vor ir ende sach
und daz er si alten
muose behalten
und geistlîchen rât geben
über sêle und über leben.
    Dannoch was ir daz unkunt,
gesach si in ie vor der stunt.
mit listen sprach er dô zuo ir:
'vrouwe, durch got saget mir,   3880
habet ir sît iht vernomen
war iuwer sun sî komen,
weder er sî lebende oder tôt?'
do ersiufte si: des gie ir nôt.
si sprach: 'herre, nein ich.
ich weiz wol, er hât an sich
von riuwen solhe nôt geleit,
ich envernemes rehte wârheit,
so engeloube ich niht daz er noch lebe.'
er sprach: 'ob daz von gotes gebe   3890
iemer möhte geschehen
daz man in iuch lieze sehen,
nû saget wie, getriuwet ir doch

As she confessed to him, he heard
The tale that from the past so well
He knew, and listening to her tell
That history so undisguised,
Then it was he realized   3860
She was his mother in verity.
The good man, loyal and trustworthy,
Rejoiced to God in gratitude
That she had thus so humbly sued
And submitted to his command,
For he could see and understand,
She had atoned and was contrite.
With ready greeting and delight
He received his mother there,
And he felt joy beyond compare   3870
To have this bliss on him descend:
Of seeing her before her end,
And being able to keep her there,
As she grew old, and give her care
And counsel of religious worth*
For her soul and life on earth.
    Still was it hid from her that she
Ever had seen him formerly.
With guarded words he then did say,
"Before God, lady, tell me, pray,   3880
Have you heard aught from anyone
Of what has happened to your son?
Is he alive, or has he died?"
The question pained her, and she sighed.
"I have not, lord," she said. "So great,
Alas, was the oppressive weight
Of his remorse and penitence,
Unless I have strong evidence,
I'll not believe he's still alive."
"If it befell him to survive,"   3890
He said, "and you, by God's great grace,
Were granted to behold his face,
Say now, could you with certainty

ob ir in erkandet noch ?'
si sprach: 'mich entriege mîn sin,
ich erkande in wol, und sæhe ich in.'
    Er sprach: 'nû saget des ich iuch bite,
weder wære iu dâ mite
liep oder leit geschehen,
ob ir in müeset sehen ?'   3900
si sprach: 'ir muget wol nemen war,
ich hân mich bewegen gar
lîbes unde guotes,
vreuden unde muotes
gelîch eim armen wîbe:
mir enmöhte ze disem lîbe
dehein vreude mê geschehen
niuwan diu, müese ich in sehen.'
    Er sprach: 'sô gehabet iuch wol,
wande ich iu vreude künden sol.   3910
ez ist unlanc daz ich in sach
und daz er mir bî gote jach
daz er deheinen vriunt hæte
ze triuwen und ze stæte
lieberen danne iuwern lîp.'
'genâde, herre,' sprach daz wîp,
'lebet er noch ?' 'jâ er'. 'nû wie ?'
'er gehabet sich wol und ist hie.'
'mac ich in gesehen, herre ?'
'jâ, wol: er ist unverre.'   3920
'herre, sô lât mich in sehen.'
'vrouwe, daz mac wol geschehen:
sît daz ir in sehen welt,
sô ist unnôt daz ir des twelt.
vil liebiu muoter, sehet mich an:
ich bin iuwer sun und iuwer man.
swie grôz und swie swære
mîner sünden last wære,
des hât nû got vergezzen
und hân alsus besezzen   3930
disen gewalt von gote.

Still recognize that it was he?"
"Unless I'm very much misled,
I'd know him upon sight," she said.
   "To what I now inquire of you,"
He said, "reply without ado:
If you could see him, would you be
Grieved or happy?" Then said she: 3900
"Surely you are full aware
That I did utterly forswear
The flesh and pleasure's appetite,
Worldly goods, joy, and delight,
And lived my life as were I poor.
No further joy, of this I'm sure,
Could come my way unless it be
That someday him again I'd see."
   He said, "Now be of peaceful mind:
I bring you news of joyous kind.   3910
I saw him a short time ago,
And he told me, God knows it's so,
No dearer friend than you had he,
Who cherished him so constantly
And loyally in every way."
Then she spoke: "Lord, I beg you, say:
Does he still live?" "He does." "But how
Is that?" "He's well and is here now."
"May I not see him, lord?" "No fear,
You may, indeed; he is quite near."   3920
"Lord, then let me see his face."
"Lady, with ease that can take place.
Since it's your wish to see him, stay!
No further need now to delay!
Beloved mother, look at me:
Your son, your husband—I am he!
Grievously though I did err,
Oppressive as my great sins were,
God has now forgiven me:
This office of authority   3930
I have assumed through God's own hand.

ez kam von sînem gebote
daz ich her wart erwelt:
alsus hân ich im geselt
beidiu sêle unde lîp.'

    Sus wart daz gnâdelôse wîp
ergetzet leides des ir war.
got samente si wunderlichen dar
ze vreuden in beiden.
sus wâren si ungescheiden   3940
unz an den gemeinen tôt.
als ir Grêgôrjus gebôt
und ir ze büezenne riet,
dô er von ir lande schiet,
mit lîbe und mit guote,
mit beitendem muote,
daz hâte si geleistet gar
sô daz ir niht dar an war.
swaz si ouch jâre sît vertriben
sît si ze Rôme ensamt beliben,   3950
diu wâren in beiden
ze gote alsô bescheiden
daz si nû iemer mêre sint
zwei ûz erweltiu gotes kint.
ouch erwarp er sînem vater daz
daz er den stuol mit im besaz
dem niemer vreude zegât:
wol im der in besezzen hât.

It came about through His command
That I was chosen here to throne.
To Him I've offered all I own,
Both my soul and body too."

> Gregorius and his mother serve God and are
> sainted.

Thus the unfortunate woman knew
For every sorrow recompense:
For God with wondrous Providence
To gladden both had sent her there.
And so the two through life did fare   3940
Unparted till the day they died.
So utterly had she complied
With Gregory's bidding and command—
When he'd departed from her land
And counseled that she steadfastly
Do penance with her property,
Her mind, and body—not a whit
Had she ever resented it.
In all the years that came and went,
That they in Rome together spent,   3950
Their lives they dedicated so,
In serving God on earth below,
That these two children of God's love
Will dwell forever as saints above.*
For his father,* too, he gained
The throne to which he had attained,
The throne of joy that's infinite:
Happy who has attained to it!

(Epilog)

Bî disen guoten mæren
von disen sündæren,   3960
wie si nâch grôzer schulde
erwurben gotes hulde,
dâ ensol niemer an
dehein sündiger man
genemen bœsez bilde,
sî er gote wilde,
daz er iht gedenkę alsô:
'nû wis dû vrävel unde vrô:
wie soldestû verwâzen wesen?
sît daz dise sint genesen   3970
nâch ir grôzen meintât,
sô wirt dîn als guot rât:
und ist daz ich genesen sol,
sô genisę ich alsô wol.'
swen des der tiuvel schündet
daz er ûf den trôst sündet,
den hât er überwunden
und in sînen gewalt gebunden:
und ist joch sîn sünde kranc,
sô kumet der selbe gedanc   3980
mit tûsentvalter missetât
und wirt sîn niemer mêre rât.
dâ sol der sündige man
ein sælic bilde nemen an,
swie vil er gesündet hât,

Epilogue

The poet reiterates the need for man to show remorse for his sins and to undergo penance. In
this way will a sinful man be saved.

From this useful story now
About these sinners*—telling how   3960
They sinned, committing heavy crime,
And still obtained God's grace in time—
Let no sinner, if he stray
And from God be turned away,
Claim an evil precedent
For furthering his own intent,
By falsely reasoning this way:
"Now you be bold, and you be gay:
Since they've been saved, of sin acquitted,
Despite the great crimes they committed,   3970
Why would you be damned? For you
There'll be as good a way out, too.
If you're to be saved, saved you'll be,
Just as well and readily."
Who heeds the Devil's spur to sin,
Relying on this to save his skin,
Him the Devil has overthrown,
Him the Devil has made his own.
And, though slight his sin may be,
A thousand sins will accompany   3980
This selfsame thought, and never more
Will there be help for him in store.
A sinful man from this tale should
This moral draw for his own good:
No matter how great his sins may be,

daz sîn doch wirt guot rât,
ob er die riuwe begât
und rehte buoze bestât.

   Hartman, der sîn arbeit
an diz liet hât geleit 3990
gotẹ und iu ze minnen,
der gert dar an gewinnen
daz ir im lât gevallen
ze lône von in allen
die ez hœren oder lesen
daz si im bittende wesen
daz im diu sælde geschehe
daz er iuch noch gesehe
in dem himelrîche.
des sendet alle gelîche 4000
disen guoten sündære
ze boten um unser swære,
daz wir in disem ellende
ein alsô genislich ende
nemen als si dâ nâmen.
des gestiurẹ uns got. âmen.

He can be saved most certainly
If genuine remorse he shows,
And then just penance undergoes.

May the reader pray for the poet's soul!

Hartmann, who berhymed this tale
With effort that it might avail 3990
To God's pleasure and to yours, too,
Desires that there may be due,
In reward for what he's done,
This reward from everyone,
From those who hear and those who read
His tale: that each one pray and plead
That this good fortune him betide:
In Heav'n he see you and abide
In that Kingdom without end.
Let all of you alike hence send 4000
This godly sinner to intercede*
For us in our distressing need,
That we in this exile of grief*
At death may likewise find relief,
And be redeemed as they were then.
May God help us to that! Amen.

Appendix

The Prologue is the most disputed portion of the text. Even in the Middle Ages it was either scorned or misunderstood, and hence either omitted—as in the case of most of the manuscripts and in the *Gesta Romanorum*— or altered to fit the conventional sermonizing approach —as in the case of Arnold von Lübeck in his Latin translation of the early thirteenth century. Even though I collated the variants of the Prologue in order to establish a reliable basis for translation, I know that ambiguities and obscurities exist in the text itself that can be clarified by no translation. Perhaps some day hitherto unknown manuscripts of *Gregorius* will come to light that will make lucid some of the dark passages.

The rhetoric of the Prologue is neither ornate nor plain but of the middle category. Characteristic is the use of doublings, antithesis, oxymoron, as well as of formalized expressions. Furthermore, parataxis and hypotaxis create difficulties of structure and interpretation that are intrinsic to the text. I tend to agree with Hendricus Sparnaay who, in his biography of Hartmann, believes that parts of the Prologue were written after the narrative of the epic was completed. On the other hand, Professor Helen Adolf points out that the charm of the Prologue lies in its gradual approach to the actual plot of the epic. The religious-didactic element and the legendary motif flow together to produce an artistic whole, heightening the anticipatory interest. (For pertinent discussion of the nature of the Prologue by comparison with that of *Parzival*, Professor Adolf's enlightening article may serve the interested reader: "Der Eingang zu Wolframs Parzival," *Neophil.* XXII [1937], 110-120; 171-185.) Nevertheless, the religious-didactic element seems to have the upper hand to such a degree that the well-known medievalist Hugo Kuhn calls the Prologue "a formal disavowal of the courtly fairy-tale."

Whether or not Hartmann divided his poem in any way is, of course, unknown. Some editors of the text, like Bech and Neumann, do divide the epic into sections with headings. Others, like Paul and Leitzmann, present the text without break. I have followed the procedure of the former, but I have made divisions where they seemed most justifiable to me. The paragraphing and punctuation are, likewise, my own. Arnold of Lübeck, in his Latin translation, divided the epic into chapters with a general introduction.

Hartmann's treatment of the religious legend is at times indeed arid and didactic. It is when he soars above the mere plot and makes his characters alive through their human frailties and emotions that he is truly the poet—not merely the fashioner of an exercise in church rules. We are moved by the baby's laughter, by the parents' tears, by the teacher's farewell to his pupil, by the love and pain human beings experience and suffer. The tone of the epic, however, stems from the exposition of faith as presented in the Prologue. Sinful man, no matter what his crime, if he but have faith, may obtain the grace of God and his own salvation through true repentance and expiation.

Notes

5. *tumben jâr* 'foolish youth.' I believe these words are no mere expression of humility; Hartmann is here voicing his own suffering and change of heart. If Hartmann's feudal lord died before *Gregorius* was begun, then surely the ensuing grief contributed to his turning away from the world and seeking solace in religious thought.

19. *êhafte nôt* 'dire necessity' is used for the French *par force*. This is a legal term for a critical state or emergency. Some commentators interpret this to mean "original sin."

22 (21). *vürgedank* 'intent' is here equivalent to *praesumptio*. The two chief sins against the Holy Ghost, as given by Petrus Lombardus in his list of six, are *praesumptio* and *desperatio*. If one arrogantly puts off making amends and continues to sin, trusting that in the hour of death one will be forgiven, one is committing the sin of *praesumptio*. If one despairs of God's mercy, thinking one's sins are too great to be forgiven, one commits the sin of *desperatio*. Hartmann is in harmony with the teaching of the medieval Church in showing how "the good sinner" is forgiven.

27. I have translated *mit Abêle* as 'a second Abel.' Literally the phrase means 'along with Abel,' but the connotation, I believe, justifies my interpretation.

35. The line begins a striking personal utterance in which Hartmann voices his feeling of guilt in having written worldly poetry. He speaks here, I feel, not only as a poet but as a man who has undergone some change of heart.

36-40. The lines probably have a double meaning. Hartmann may mean that he intends to write such poetry as would correspond with God's will, and/or to write in order that God's will may be made manifest.

44-50. The hypotactic and paratactic construction of this sentence has led me to rearrange the clauses in English for better logical sequence.

47 (49). *riuwe* 'remorse.' The word means not only suffering or painful sorrow but also the *contritio cordis* 'interior, super-

natural, universal, and sovereign' sorrow that "comes from the heart and not merely from the lips."

64. *zwîvel* 'sinful doubting and despair.' It is "the great enemy of the soul, the bane of spiritual life," writes Professor Helen Adolf. In the religious sense, the word means the sin of *desperatio*. I have translated it with a hendiadys in an attempt to give the full meaning of the word.

65. *versenket* 'downfall' is used with theological connotation to mean the fall of the soul into a state of sin. Whether or not Hartmann himself experienced conflict between the pull of the spiritual realm and that of this world has been the subject of controversy. The word occurs with this meaning again in line 2603.

66-78. These lines are believed by some to describe the first steps of the sacrament of penance in the Church: 1) Examination of conscience 2) Contrition 3) Resolution never more to offend God 4) Confession of sins to the priests 5) Acceptance of penance for sins.

73. *wider komen*. This refers to God's grace and not to resurrection; hence, I have translated "return to grace."

74. See note to line 64.

79. With reference to the oxymoron, comparison may be made with the famous elegy of Walther von der Vogelweide. Lamenting that we are so easily poisoned by pleasures, he writes: "ich sihe die gallen mitten in dem henege sweben" 'And in the midst of pleasures, sweet as honey, I see man's falseness, bitter as gall' (my translation). The gall-honey antithesis occurs again in line 456. It is a favorite one with Hartmann, stemming from church literature. The Latin *mel* 'honey' and *fel* 'gall' provide an obvious rhyme.

87-89. Ultimately this becomes Gregorius' road as it leads him to the fisherman who is instrumental in directing him to his way of penance.

97 ff. Hartmann's characters are individuals rather than stereotypes. It is Gregorius, not the Good Samaritan, who is the subject of the parable. As Professor Adolf has stated, the treatment of the Good Samaritan anticipates the course of the epic.

113. *gedingen unde vorhte* 'hope and fear' are here not merely human emotions; they are allegorical figures and show how the human is bound to the divine. The level of discourse is theological, not courtly.

131-134. Although oil and wine were used by medieval physicians in the treatment of wounds, here, of course, the oil is the symbol of the Holy Spirit; the wine symbolizes the purifying effect of God's Law or Teaching.

166. Not to trust God is to despair of God's grace. This is blasphemy against the Holy Ghost. See Matt. 12.31-32. See also the note to line 64. Medieval man was deeply disturbed by the danger of his falling into a state of despair if he sinned against the Holy Ghost.

236. A young heiress was not safe in the Middle Ages. The father should have betrothed her early, since her life and land would be endangered at his death.

323. *minne* is here *concupiscentia*. This kind of love, particularly in conjunction with *vrou* 'lady' in *Gregorius* is thought of as sinful. See also line 451. In *hohe minne* there is an idealization of womankind.

326. Cf. 11, 303 ff. It is the nature of the Devil to lead man to disgraceful action. The attempt at an analysis of what led the brother on to commit incest is not successful. Hartmann simply enumerates four stimuli without integrating them cogently.

384. Hartmann is not consistent in presenting the sister as completely naïve!

437. She will die a physical death, a death of the body, scorned by this world; and her soul will be condemned on Judgment Day.

456. See note to line 79.

463. *arbeit*. Although the word frequently involves ethical principles, it is simply 'suffering,' 'misery' in this line.

470 (471). *gotes hulde*. By this is meant God's grace or favor that gives the soul its salvation in eternal life. One commentator maintains that Hartmann's epics follow a pattern, in

that his heroes go through a development from *Ehre* 'honorable and respected position' to *Sünde* 'state of sin' to *Leid* 'suffering' to *Busse* 'penance' to *Gnade* 'state of grace.' Grace appears as a miracle that leads the knight back to *êre* and activity in the world.

475-477. Although it was the popular impression that a child born of incest was itself sinful, Hartmann knew better, since he was familiar with the Church teaching.

512. One asks oneself why he was not sent for sooner!

517. Not all rooms in a medieval castle were heated! A *kemenâte* usually had a fireplace.

609-624 (607-624). This is a famous play on the words *guot, muot.* To our feeling a play on words at this point in the story injects a frivolous note, but in the Middle Ages such a play on significant words was not felt as inappropriate but rather as heightening of the intensity of the connotations. A translation of *muot* as "moods" to rhyme with "goods" produces not only a distortion of rhyme but also a distortion in the meaning of *muot.* The English cognate "mood" translates *muot* only rarely, whereas the New High German *Mut* is often an adequate equivalent.

671. *der guote sündaere.* The English title of Thomas Mann's *Der Erwählte, The Holy Sinner,* may have been influential in the choice of "holy" in some translations. However, "holy" does not seem to me to be quite appropriate, and I have used the simpler form of the oxymoron, "the good sinner."

684. They have faith that God will direct them step by step; but again, as in line 512, one may wonder why the deliberation did not take place earlier.

700. Exposure of an unwanted child was common practice in this period, but ordinarily the infant was placed at the doorstep of a church or monastery.

734-766. The inscription on the tablet is significant in the development of the epic. Gregorius is to avoid the sin of *superbia.* The knowledge of his antecedents may free him from *hubris* and turn his mind and heart to God. If he is to make atonement for his parents' sinning and to intercede for them *zaller stunde* 'constantly,' he can best do so by a life of humility and prayer within the Church—certainly not so easily in the world of knighthood. Within the world he exposes himself to relationships that may prove to be incestuous. The tablet thus prescribes the ideal behavior for Gregorius. Subsequently, by an act of free will he rejects his mother's guidance, and by choosing knighthood he fails of perfection and falls into sin.

746. *diu buoch lêrte.* It may mean to "teach him to read." *buoch* frequently means the Holy Books; i.e., Scriptures. To interpret it in this way would allow him to learn to read and would strengthen the mother's recommendation that he turn aside from the world and cultivate a religious life.

757 (756). The child is to act as an intercessor!

798. This particularly significant line has been used in determining the chronology of Hartmann's works.

805-806. *leid* is the consequence of sin in the spiritual-religious sense. It is also a means of atonement; hence, it is a way out of sin. The variant readings give the number of sorrows both as three and as four. This may be another instance of the symbolic use of number. If Manuscript A is to be accepted, the symbolism may be with the number "four"; more likely is the trinity symbolism. With reference to number symbolism, it is well to remember a remark of Schwietering's in which he states that he is anxious to avoid over-emphasis of the significance of *Zahlenmystik*, "because more people are able to count than to weigh."

843 (844). See line 301 in which she loves him more.

852. *herzeriuwe.* This is the deadly suffering and sorrow of love.

855. A woman who gave birth to a male child had to wait thirty-three days before she was permitted to attend church service. Gregorius is thirty days old when the death of his father is reported. See Levit. 12.2-4.

856. *klage.* This is the term that is usually associated with death and burial.

872. *helt.* The picture of God is that of a feudal lord, the

mightiest and best of heroes. If Hartmann, in *Gregorius*, has turned from love of woman to love of God, then there may well be a strong empathetic element in lines 871-898.

944. *ein geistlich abbet* makes the abbot a true priest and not merely a nobleman not trained within the Church; or the expression may mean that as abbot he is a deeply devout priest.

1025. *crêde mich*. The abbot uses the Latin word *crede* which governs the dative case. The German *mich* is probably the Latin dative *mihi* with a syncope of the final *i*, giving *mih* which was sounded like *mich*, rhyming with *sich*. The Latin word should be retained in the English, of course.

1048 (1047). *tougen* is literally 'secretly, to oneself'; hence my "silently."

1052. *phelle* is a general term for fine silks and brocades that at this time came from the East, often from Alexandria, by way of Venice.

1077. It is not clear why it should seem reasonable to "people" that the poorer brother should rear his niece's son.

1085. The christening took place after the midday meal. Mass was celebrated in the morning.

1112. It would be customary among the peasantry for husband and wife to attend church with the child for its christening.

1132-1133. The fishermen are serfs, bound to the abbey by feudal law. I have kept *gotes hûses* to stress the idea that the people belong to the monastery.

1135. Technically the abbot's sponsorship is a moot point! According to one authority, the abbot could act as godfather, but he could not then baptize the child himself. According to canon law, therefore, the abbot acts as godfather *per nefas!* The legendary element is evidently quite strong at this point.

1136. "Gregorius" and "Gregory" will be used interchangeably in accordance with metrical needs.

1158. A monastery lad would begin his studies at the age of eight.

1181-1200. In the trivium Gregorius would have studied ethics, since the latter was included both in grammar and in rhetoric. He would have studied *divinitas*, moral philosophy as well as theology. In courtly rhetoric, a legal argument often had as its subject the analysis of guilt motifs.

1235. *vrouwe Sælicheit*, which I have given as Lady Bountiful, is a difficult concept to translate. "Lady Blessedness" is too awkward an expression in English and does not necessarily convey the idea of her bestowing happiness upon others.

1262 (1263). *Wunsche.* This is likewise a difficult word to translate. It must be a personification but as such it must obtain God's permission for the execution of its work. *Perfection* seems closer in its connotations as the embodiment of all that is admirable and desirable.

1278-1280. The fact that Gregorius was supposedly of humble fisherfolk parentage made it impossible for people to say that he was nobly born; that was a pity, for Gregorius really behaved like a child of noble birth.

1305. *bî jenem sê.* The use of the demonstrative localizes the occurrence; the phrase means simply "along the sea."

1323. *vuntkint* 'foundling.' This is a new substantive compounded by Hartmann. It is the significance of this word that in part explains the foster mother's passionate outburst. Today it is a misfortune but no disgrace to be a foundling. In the twelfth century a foundling was indeed the meanest of lowly creatures. Foundlings were considered in the same class with thieves, murderers, jugglers, strolling louts. Many criminals were actual foundlings. Not to have blood relations was almost a crime in itself. On the other hand, of course, there were the flourishing Venetian monasteries for foundlings, institutions from which certain "foundlings" (?) could rise to positions of eminence.

1346. Legally a foundling belonged to whoever found it and took care of it, provided no claim was made within ten days. Since the fisherman found Gregorius, the wife regrets that her husband relinquished Gregorius to the abbot. Legally, however, the fisherman belonged to the monastery!

1353. The legal idea here involved is that the sea belongs to everybody; hence, the fisherman's wife feels that Gregorius is her husband's property.

1373. See note to line 1323.

1437 (1436)-1449. This is one of the most significant passages dealing with free will. It is the clear presentation of the Augustinian point of view. Gregorius' suffering is the result of his own choice. His guilt lies in his voluntary decision to enter upon the life of knighthood in spite of the fact that he knows of his history.

1449 (1448). The explication of this line does not come until lines 1517 ff.

1507. Here the monastic life is called the sweetest life of all. Lines 1531-1533 say that there is no better life than the life of knighthood; lines 2222-2224 say that lawful wedlock is the best life God has given man. This is really medieval gradualism. Each *gradus* 'order' has its own code of perfection. Hartmann may himself have hesitated or vacillated between two callings.

1535. Hartmann is saying that it is better to be a true *miles dei* 'knight of God' than a hypocritical monk; more can be done for the glory of God as a proper knight than by such a monk in the Church.

1547-1738. These lines appear here for the first time in English metrical form. They were omitted in the Zeydel-Morgan translation. They explain Gregorius' ardent desire to become a knight and vividly describe the picture he sees of himself. The romantic ideals of the young lad are balanced by the rational advice of the abbot. The passage is full of pithy, aphoristic turns, and gives a touching portrayal of young Gregorius.

1570 (1569). To be able to tell good from evil is not a matter of being old in years! Gregorius then was about eleven years of age. In *Der arme Heinrich* the girl, likewise, is eleven years old—the age of discretion.

1625 ff. Hartmann's humor is evident in these lines. As a cloister-trained poet he is well aware of what is spoken in the

Church. The German he refers to is the new vocabulary of the chivalric world which entered Germany by way of France. Hartmann has his tongue in cheek. The *aventiûre* and its language were not closed books to the clergy! The term "Greek" is used in the Latin literature of the period to characterize what is not understood.

1628. See note to line 1025.

1647. In "dubbing" Gregorius knight, the abbot is acting in the role of a princely lord. If he were a simple churchman, he would not have such authority.

1677. Gregorius in this passage shuns *gemach,* the indolent comfort and ease that keep a knight from knightly deeds.

1698. *diu Sælde.* I translate this, as I did *vrouwe Sælicheit,* by Lady Bountiful. Unfortunately, the connotation of bliss is lost.

1771. Churchmen were not allowed to earn interest on money (usury). How the abbot managed to increase Gregorius' original capital is not made clear. It would be completely impossible for an abbot to have the "profession" of a money-lender.

1780. Gregorius feels guilt though he has done no wrong. Here some scholars see the workings of original sin.

1789. The abbot means that each day of knighthood will add to the weight of guilt that Gregorius already bears. By turning from the life of a religious, he exposes himself to greater sinfulness.

1796 (1795). *hie ze klage.* The abbot, speaking for the Church, as a representative of God, could ask Gregorius to submit to His judgment in the monastery. He does not mean that God is called upon to make judgment during Gregorius' life on earth. There are only two judgments: judgment upon death, and that on Judgment Day.

1835. By having the ship go where the winds drive it, Gregorius is putting himself into God's hands.

1920 (1919). Everyone stood in church, since this was in the time before pews.

1942-1954. It is significant that the mother does not immediately question the origin of such familiar fabrics. She is, of course, reminded of her *leit* 'sorrow'; but there may be some element of negative will—possibly a semi-conscious desire not to see her child in the knight. She has vowed never to marry. In breaking her vow she is guilty of *praesumptio*. The way of redemption described in the Prologue becomes even more applicable to the mother than to Gregorius himself.

1999. Hartmann suddenly makes the unnamed foe, hitherto simply a mighty lord, a Roman duke!

2081. It was customary for a knight to attend early mass before going out to meet an opponent.

2098-2099. Those who are in attendance on the duke allow him to fight in single combat. There would be no glory for the duke if he let his men attack Gregorius. Hence, they are showing their respect in giving him the opportunity to get the better of Gregorius without their aid.

2274-2275. In practicing the knightly virtue of *mâze* 'proper moderation' for the glory of God, Gregorius was satisfied to rule over only those lands that owed him allegiance, instead of going out to conquer all his neighbors—it is obvious that he could have overcome all of them!

2391-2394. Stylistically, these lines are typical of the religious poetry of the period.

2577. It would have been catastrophic (if not impossible) for a noblewoman of the Middle Ages to marry a commoner.

2656 ff. The soul and body are meant, not the mother and her son. In this significant passage, Hartmann voices the conflict that exists between the flesh and the spirit. He is not always an exponent of the ascetic point of view, and he is not always so pessimistic.

2678. The line refers particularly to the suffering of the soul in purgatory.

2684-2694. The wavering, uncertain speech discloses the mother's fear and hope, as well as her diffidence about asking her son for help. At the same time, it gives Hartmann the opportunity of restating his religious belief. When she says "sun herre," she means that Gregorius is her son, of course, but she means also that he is her superior; through his marriage, he is her lord and master; through his monastery training, he is an educated man.

2751 ff. From this point on, Gregorius' *arbeit* is that of being penitent in all humility. On renouncing the knightly life he once chose, he enters upon the bitter road that leads to ultimate bliss. *arbeit* here connotes the intentional suffering Gregorius chooses to undergo for the sake of the development of his moral life. Knighthood gives way to the need for God's grace.

2852. All beggars were thought of as messengers of God. A devout woman would readily feel the need to be kind to beggars.

2915. *gelimet*. The toes are close together, not spread as they would be in someone who habitually walked barefoot.

3047 ff. The deep sleep that comes after long prayers and weariness makes it plausible that Gregorius forgets his ivory tablet.

3119. *trôstgeist* 'The Holy Ghost.' This is the Third Person of the Trinity. It can be sent by Christ, or by the Father upon request of the Son, or it is breathed out by Christ.

3133. It was part of the religious faith of the period to give credit to miracles. Although Hartmann considered magic in the light of madness and superstition, he did believe deeply in the teachings of the Church. Here Hartmann denounces the sceptic or disbeliever.

3289. The line indicates that the two noble Romans had attendants with them. It means literally: They bade them (their servants) pay him for the fish.

3291. Since the whole fish would taste bitter if the gall were broken, the experienced fisherman is asked to clean the fish.

3331-3345. The two noblemen were priests, for in line 3655 they share their priestly garb with Gregorius. However, a formal confession could be made to only one priest and one priest alone. Yet Hartmann probably meant the act of the fisher to be the *confessio*. It is difficult to interpret *mit geistlîchen triuwen* since it may go with the fisher or with the priests. I have attempted to preserve the ambiguity, considering it the reaction of both the fisher and priests, as individuals, and as characteristic of the priests' profession. Thus, when the fisher carries out the recommendations of the priests, he is performing the act of *satisfactio*. The three steps of penance are thus taken: through the heart, *per contritionem*, through the mouth, *per confessionem*, through works, *per satisfactionem*.

3374. *die boume*. Here the word probably does not mean 'trees' but some sort of pole, or spar. The word could mean *Segelbäume;* the sails would be lowered on approaching shore, and there would be difficulty in landing.

3379-3400. This passage illustrates Hartmann's tendency to use extensive antithesis for rhetorical effect. It is the longest negative description in any of the courtly epics. For the sake of clarity in English, I have introduced the negative decription by "Perhaps you think" in line 3379. I have punctuated with question marks in order to heighten the reader's awareness of the antithesis. Middle High German does this through the use of the subjunctive, but since we lack a full subjunctive in English, the series of positive assertions, couched in the indicative for the most part, would weaken, I believe, the antithetical irony.

3473-3475. Gregorius had retained all the learning that he had once gained from books.

3501 ff. In refraining from looking at human beings, and in addressing them as Christians, Gregorius may be indicating that he considers himself in the state of excommunication.

3520. Gregorius thinks of himself as tainted, almost as if he were a leper and would contaminate others through his presence.

3571-3572. This was the prevalent church belief and teaching.

3585. The line must mean that Gregorius, despite his shackles, was able to turn aside or to go a short distance.

3610. That is, Christ.

3617 (3616). Gregorius is excluding the fisher from his count, or he is counting the two priests as one entity. The use of three, instead of the logical four, may again be symbolical, particularly since the Paraclete has just been mentioned.

3765. To show respect for a new ruler who was coming from outside the country, his subjects would march in solemn procession toward the border to welcome him.

3768-3769. It was, and still is, customary in religious processions to hold aloft sacred relics enclosed in a box, the shrine.

3805. *stole* is here used to symbolize the ecclesiastical judicial power.

3824. *über geistlichez leben* refers to the whole realm of spiritual life. As pope, Gregorius would deal not only with the priests of the Church but also with the rest of the world.

3875. He would give her not only his counsel and advice but also the consolation of absolution.

3954. Both Gregorius and his mother become saints.

3955. The line can mean only Gregorius' real father, not the abbot.

3960. Gregorius and his parents are meant.

4001 (4002). Only saints can be intercessors.

4003. *ellende* 'another country, living out of one's country, banishment.' I have translated it as "exile of grief," since in the religious sense, one is an exile from Heaven as long as one is on earth.

4005. In *Gregorius* Hartmann is portraying the conflict between God's law and the demands of the ethics of knighthood. He does not negate the role of knighthood in the world, but he does point out its questionable nature, viewed from a deeper level of being. In a sense, he is stating a profound insight about man: when man is unable to solve the overwhelming problems that face him, he seeks saintliness for his own salvation. Out of the depths of calamity and helplessness, when life no longer seems possible, rises the saint, secure in his knowledge of self and of God.